INTRODUCTION
TO
SYMBOLIC LOGIC

INTRODUCTION
TO
SYMBOLIC LOGIC

BY

A. H. BASSON, B.A.
LECTURER IN PHILOSOPHY AT UNIVERSITY COLLEGE, LONDON

AND

D. J. O'CONNOR, M.A., Ph.D.
PROFESSOR OF PHILOSOPHY IN THE UNIVERSITY OF EXETER

UNIVERSITY TUTORIAL PRESS LTD
CLIFTON HOUSE, EUSTON ROAD, LONDON, N.W.1

Published 1953
Second Edition 1957
Third Edition 1959
Reprinted 1962, 1965

PRINTED IN GREAT BRITAIN BY UNIVERSITY TUTORIAL PRESS LTD, FOXTON
NEAR CAMBRIDGE

PREFACE TO THE THIRD EDITION

THIS book provides the beginner in formal logic with a short introduction that is thorough enough on important points to offer a basis for the study of more advanced works. The first four chapters give an account of the calculus of propositions, and the next two give an outline of the predicate calculus in which special attention is given to the basic notion of satisfiability. An appendix sketches the traditional doctrine of the syllogism and its relation to the Boolean algebra of classes. No previous knowledge of logic is assumed, although the historical first section of Chapter I will be of interest chiefly to those students who have some acquaintance with the traditional logic of the syllogism.

Chapter IV was extensively revised for the Second Edition. The present edition incorporates a number of minor corrections and amendments. We are grateful to reviewers for criticisms and suggestions.

Bibliographical notes to the chapters have been added to guide the students' further reading and exercises have been provided. It should be emphasised that the working of exercises is just as essential to the understanding of the bookwork in elementary logic as it is in mathematics.

A. H. B.
D. J. O'C.

CONTENTS

INTRODUCTION TO SYMBOLIC LOGIC

CHAPTER I

INTRODUCTORY

1. Symbolic Logic and Classical Logic. Symbolic logic has a short history and the traditional or classical Aristotelian logic has a long one. Yet the difference between them is only that of different stages of development. Classical logic is related to symbolic logic as embryo to adult organism. It is necessary to emphasise this point at the outset as there has been a certain amount of controversy over the nature and standing of symbolic logic, especially during the last fifty years. Philosophical logicians, trained in the classical logic, have sometimes criticised the work of the symbolic logicians on the ground that it involved misconceptions about the nature of logic. And symbolic logicians have sometimes criticised the defects of the traditional logic as though it were quite outmoded.

It is now generally agreed by logicians that modern symbolic logic is a development of concepts and techniques which were implicit in the work of Aristotle. But this fact was for a long time obscured by the curious history of the subject. The foundations of logic were so brilliantly and thoroughly laid by Aristotle in the fourth century B.C. that it seemed to most of Aristotle's successors to be a finished science. It is now realised that his treatment covered only a small (though important) branch of logic. Moreover, the very thoroughness of his achievement was a part cause of the failure of logicians to make any significant contributions to the subject during the next two thousand years.

Recent studies in the history of logic have shown that both the Greek successors of Aristotle and the medieval scholastics made several important logical discoveries. But the importance of these discoveries was not generally realised at the time at which they were made and, in consequence, they failed to initiate any renascence in the development of logical theory and technique. The reason for this was two-fold. The general belief that all the important logical discoveries had been made by Aristotle naturally tended to prevent philosophers from assessing any new discovery at its true value. But a second and more important reason was the undeveloped state of the mathematical sciences prior to the seventeenth century.

Aristotle had introduced into logic the important notion of a *variable*. This notion is to-day quite a familiar one to educated men and women because they meet it in the schoolroom when they are taught elementary algebra. A variable is a symbol which can stand for any one of a given range of values. Thus, if $x^2 = 4$, and x is a variable which ranges over the real numbers, the equation is true for just two values of the variable, that is, when x takes one of the two values $+2$ or -2. The use of variables in elementary mathematics is too familiar to need comment. But it has become familiar through the development and dissemination of mathematical knowledge. Aristotle's use of variables in logic was restricted to representing the terms used in syllogistic arguments by letters of the alphabet, in order to bring out more clearly the logical structure of arguments of this type. But the use of variables in symbolic logic is much wider than this. Nor was this the only way in which the development of mathematics contributed to the renascence of logic.

A distinguished modern logician* has cited three characteristics of symbolic logic:

* C. I. Lewis.

(1) The use of *ideograms* or signs which stand directly for concepts, instead of *phonograms* or signs which stand directly for sounds and only indirectly for concepts. For example, the multiplication sign ($\times$) or the question mark (?) are ideograms, as are the written characters of the Chinese language. But the written *words* "multiplication sign" or "question mark" *directly* represent the spoken English words which correspond to them, as do the words in all languages which are written according to some sort of phonetic rules.

(2) The *deductive method*. This is familiar from school geometry. The characteristic of the method is that from a small number of statements we can generate, by the application of a limited number of rules, an indefinite number of other statements, often new and surprising.

(3) The use of *variables* having a definite range of significance. (This point has been mentioned already.)

Now these three characteristics of symbolic logic are also, as is obvious, characteristics of mathematics. Thus the development of symbolic logic has been bound up with the development of mathematics and it is significant that all the pioneers of the subject were either mathematicians or philosophers with a training in mathematical methods and an appreciation of them.

The first important name in the development of logic from its traditional classical form into its modern symbolic form is that of G. W. von Leibniz (1646-1716). He is celebrated equally as a philosopher and as a mathematician, being best known as the co-inventor, with Newton, of the differential calculus. Before he was twenty years of age, he published a book entitled *Dissertatio de Arte Combinatoria*, in which he put forward a two-fold plan for the reform of logic. He suggested first the establishment of a universal scientific language (*characteristica universalis*) in which all scientific concepts could be represented by a combination of basic *ideograms*. Apart from the proposal to replace phonograms by ideograms this proposal belongs rather to linguistics than to logic. But his second proposal is more important. He suggested that a universal calculus of reasoning (*calculus ratiocinator*) could be devised which would provide an automatic method of solution for all problems which could be expressed in the universal language. Had he carried out his proposal, he would have provided a system of symbolic logic. But his plan remained a mere suggestion which was not developed.

The next important name in the development of symbolic logic is that of George Boole (1815-64). Boole was a mathematician who held the chair of mathematics at Queen's College, Cork. His contribution consisted in the formulation of a system of algebra in which the variables stand for classes and the operations of "multiplication" and "addition" represent the various ways of combining classes to make further classes. (The system will be explained in the Appendix.) The system was first set out in a small book entitled *The Mathematical Analysis of Logic* which was published in 1847 and in a subsequent work, *The Laws of Thought*, Boole applied his algebra to several branches of logic including the syllogism of the classical logic. This was an important advance in that he showed that the doctrine of the Aristotelian syllogism which had hitherto been regarded as practically co-extensive with deductive logic could be shown to be a special case of a kind of logical algebra. And it was not long before Boole's successors showed that Boole's algebra, in turn, was only one of the symbolic calculi making up the body of logic.

Other important work of nineteenth-century logicians included that of Augustus de Morgan (1806-71) on the logic of *relations* and of W. S. Jevons (1835-82) who simplified and developed Boole's algebra of classes. But the most important name is that of an American, C. S. Peirce (1839-1914), who, in a long series of papers, largely unpublished, made far-reaching contributions to almost every branch of logic. The magnitude of his achievement was realised only in the present century when his collected works were published.

In the meantime, a number of mathematicians on the continent of Europe were interesting themselves in the foundations of mathematics. Their work, in particular that of Gottlob Frege and Guiseppe Peano, was continued by Bertrand Russell, now Lord Russell. In 1910, in collaboration with A. N. Whitehead, he published *Principia Mathematica*, a monumental work in which a system of symbolic logic is elaborated and made to serve as the foundation of the whole of mathematics. The system of symbolic or mathematical logic set out by Russell and Whitehead embodied and consolidated the work of their predecessors and brought to the public notice the metamorphosis of logic which had taken place during the previous century. Since the publication of *Principia Mathematica*, logic has been a vigorously growing science.

Thus the slow and largely unnoticed development of logic since the days of Leibniz culminated in a work whose main object was mathematical. But, of course, symbolic logic is not important only for studies in the foundations of mathematics, though this is one field in which it can be useful. It shares with the traditional logic the function of providing a method of testing the validity of the arguments of ordinary language and, indeed, it offers methods of deciding the validity of types of argument which cannot be tested by the classical logic. It provides, further, a procedure for analysing the structure of propositions.* This

* See Chapter II, Section 1, for an explanation of the term "proposition".

is often convenient and sometimes necessary in philosophical argument, where the imperfections and ambiguities of everyday expression are apt to obscure the meaning of our statements. In fact, as we might expect if symbolic logic is a developed form of the classical logic, it does all the tasks which the classical logic did and many others of which classical logic was not capable.

2. The Use of Symbols. One of the functions of elementary logic is to provide methods of testing the validity of arguments. In order to do this, we have to be able to classify arguments into different *types* or *kinds* such that each specimen of a given type has certain features in common with others of the same type. The features which arguments have in common in this way are called the *logical form* of the argument. We shall be discussing logical form in the next section and need not say anything further about it here. But the traditional method of classifying arguments into types or kinds which was first invented by Aristotle involves the use of *symbols*. Consider, for example, the two following pairs of arguments:

(1) No capitalist societies are stable and some capitalist societies are democracies; therefore some democracies are not stable.

(2) No negroes are Popes and some negroes are Mohammedans; therefore some Mohammedans are not Popes.

(3) If the price of gold rises, then imports will increase. But imports will not increase. Therefore the price of gold will not rise.

(4) If the valley was caused by glaciation, then scratched boulders will be found there. But no scratched boulders are found there. Therefore the valley was not caused by glaciation.

If we examine these arguments, it is easy to see (*a*) that they are valid, and (*b*) that there are resemblances between (1) and (2) and between (3) and (4). Now these resemblances are not in the subject-matter of the argument. For the subject-matter of (1) has nothing to do with the subject-matter of (2). Nor has the subject-matter of (3) anything to do with that of (4). But if we replace the three *terms* in arguments (1) and (2) by the letters A, B, and C, the resemblance between them comes out very clearly. For both (1) and (2) now become:

(5) No A's are B's and some A's are C's; therefore some C's are not B's.

Likewise, if we replace the constituent statements of (3) and (4) by the letters *p* and *q*, we have:

(6) If *p*, then *q*. But not-*q*. Therefore, not-*p*.

Thus the use of symbols (in this case, letters of the alphabet) enables us to bring out the features of logical importance in arguments and so to classify them into types to which we can apply general rules.

The symbols used in the examples given above are *variables* because they can stand indifferently for *any* terms in the one case, or *any* statements in the other. The use of variables in logic enables us to state *general rules* for testing the validity of arguments. Hence we can say that *any* argument whatever of the type: "if no A's are B's and some A's are C's, then some C's are not B's", is a valid argument. And any argument whatever of the type: "If *p*, then *q*: but not-*q*. Therefore not-*p*" is similarly valid. Thus one important function of symbols in logic is to express the generality of the rules of logic. But it is by no means their only function. A second and almost equally important use of symbols in logic is to give conciseness and economy of expression to complicated statements which would be difficult or impossible to understand if they were expressed in ordinary language. This use of symbols is obvious in elementary algebra. Consider the following pair of equivalent expressions:

(7) The product of the sum and the difference of two numbers is equal to the difference of the squares of the two numbers.

(8) $(a + b)(a - b) = (a^2 - b^2)$.

It calls for a certain mental effort to grasp the meaning of (7) whereas (8) is immediately clear to anyone who is acquainted with the use of the symbols involved. And where the expressions are more complex, the locutions of ordinary language are far too long and involved to express their meanings clearly. It would be possible to express, without the use of mathematical symbols, a statement like the following: "the roots of the equation $ax^2 + bx + c = 0$ are given by the formula $x = \dfrac{-b \pm \sqrt{b^2 - 4ac}}{2a}$." But the corresponding linguistic expression would be so extremely cumbrous that it would be psychologically very difficult to understand it. The advantages of conciseness and clarity which the use of symbols gives to us become even more marked with more sophisticated types of mathematical reasoning. Perhaps it is possible, in theory, to express any mathematical formula or calculation in everyday language without the aid of a special symbolism. But if we were to try to do this, the limits of practical intelligibility would very soon be reached. To understand the expressions of mathematics and to work with them, we need a special symbolism. And the same is true of logic once we go beyond its very simplest levels.

Nor are these the only advantages of logical symbolism. In every science there are special technical terms which express concepts peculiar to the science in question. And these technical terms in mathematics and logic are often most conveniently symbolised by a special ideographic notation. The most famous example of a new concept symbolised by a special ideogram is the zero sign in arithmetic. Greek and Roman arithmetical notation lacked any symbol for "zero" and, in consequence, simple arithmetical calculations like "6032×54" or "2425 divided by 25", which can nowadays be performed by a ten-year old schoolboy, demanded considerable mathematical ability and an enormous amount of labour. And we have only to consider what mathematical calculation would be like if we lacked special signs like multiplication and addition signs, indices, integral signs and the like, to see the importance of special ideograms to represent the operations of mathematical calculation. In logic, we shall also need symbols to represent *logical operations* in addition to the *variables* mentioned above.

3. Logical Form. We have said enough about the use of symbols in logic to show that it is not merely pedantry to have a symbolic language into which we can translate the logical material which we have to treat. On the contrary, it is necessary for the comprehension and development of logic that we should have such a language. We must now revert to a very important topic which was referred to briefly in the preceding section, the question of *logical form*.

The distinction between the material of which a thing is made and the form, shape, or organisation of the thing is a distinction familiar to common sense. A sculptor can model a bust in clay or marble or wood or any other plastic material. The *form* or shape which he imposes on his material is the same in each case but the material differs. Conversely, the same material may be given or may take many different forms. A piece of lead may be moulded how we please under the influence of heat and pressure.

And water may be converted to ice or to steam by a change
of temperature. The notion of logical form is merely an
extension, by analogy or metaphor, of this common-sense
notion.

Such a metaphorical extension of the notion of form or
structure is familiar from other contexts. It is customary
to speak of a piece of music being in sonata form or a
poem being in sonnet form, where the notion of form is
extended or generalised to apply to things other than
material objects. And we apply, analogously, the concept
of *structure*, used originally with respect to material objects
like buildings or organisms, to entities which are not
thought of as material when we speak of "the structure of
society" or "the structure of the unconscious mind".

We are not, therefore, stretching the concept unduly in
talking of *logical* form or structure. The structure, form,
or organisation of a thing is constituted by the way in
which its parts are put together and by the mutual relations
between the parts. Thus we can speak of the logical form
of a statement or of the set of statements constituting an
argument and, in doing so, we are intending to distinguish
the *form* or *structure* of the statement or argument from
its *subject-matter*. Thus in the examples (1) and (2) in
Section 2 above, the terms "capitalist societies", "stable
societies", and "democracies" on the one hand, and
"negroes", "Popes", and "Mohammedans" on the other,
convey the subject-matter of the argument. But the
sentence "If no A's are B's and some A's are C's, then
some C's are not B's" gives us the form of the argument,
showing the relations between its constituent parts. It will
be seen in later chapters how we are concerned in logic
only with the form of arguments and not in any way with
their subject-matter. This is one of the reasons why we can
dispense with the words which refer to the subject-matter
and replace them by variables.

It will be seen that the subject of the last section, the use of symbols in logic, and the subject of logical form, are closely connected. In the elementary stages of logic, one of the main uses of a good symbolic notation is to dissect out, as it were, and to display clearly the logical form of the material with which we are dealing. And one of the advantages of symbolic logic over its less developed classical form is that it has a more complete symbolic repertory which enables us to exhibit the logical forms of arguments for which Aristotelian logic had no place. (Even so simple an argument as : "If London is larger than Paris and Paris is larger than Rome, then London is larger than Rome", cannot be assimilated to the standard forms of the classical logic.)

But why should logicians be interested in logical forms? The answer is: because the validity of arguments depends on their logical forms, and as logicians, we are interested in *validity*. This may seem, at first sight, a surprising answer. It may be thought that as we reason and debate only in order to arrive at true conclusions, the main interest of the logician should be *truth* rather than *validity*. But it is obvious on reflection that two conditions are necessary to guarantee the truth of the conclusion of any piece of reasoning. First, the evidence or *premisses* from which we make our deductions must be *true*. And, secondly, the deductions themselves must be correct or *valid*. Of these two conditions, logic can guarantee only the second. The truth of those propositions which are not formally deducible from other propositions has to be established by means which lie outside the scope of formal logic. And lest it should be thought surprising that the question of truth can be divided from the question of validity in this way, it is worth emphasising that there is in fact very little connection between these two questions.

It is obvious that in the case of *invalid* argument there is no necessary connection between the truth or falsity of the premisses and the truth or falsity of the conclusion drawn from these premisses. The premisses and conclusion may present any of the four possible combinations, true, true; true, false; false, true; and false, false. This is why invalid arguments are of no use or interest. But the case of valid arguments is not, at first sight, so very different. Of the four possible combinations of truth and falsity of premisses and conclusion, only one is impossible, namely, the case where the premisses are true and the conclusion is false. Any of the other three combinations may occur. It may seem unlikely that we can argue validly from *false* premisses to a *true* conclusion. But the following is clearly a valid argument:

All Roman emperors were presidents of the U.S.A.

Lincoln was a Roman emperor.

Therefore: Lincoln was a president of the U.S.A.

And the conclusion is true, notwithstanding the falsity of both of the premisses and the validity of the argument.

In fact, the guarantee conferred by the validity of an argument is merely this: if the premisses of a valid argument are true, the conclusion is certainly true also. But where the premisses are not true, we do not know whether the conclusion is true or false even if we are assured that the argument is valid. Thus logic does not concern itself directly with the *factual* truth of statements, even if those statements are premisses or conclusions of arguments. And it is concerned with truth indirectly only in so far as it is the consequence of the validity of an argument that, given the truth of the premisses, we may assume the truth of the conclusion.*

* We shall see later that the validity of an argument is closely associated with the *logical* truth of certain statements. But this is quite another matter.

We shall therefore be concerned, in the following chapters, with methods of testing the validity of various forms of argument. These methods will involve attention to the *logical structure* or *logical form* of arguments in that the validity of an argument is dependent on certain features of its logical form. And in order to abstract from the subject-matter of arguments and attend to the logical form alone it will be convenient to represent all arguments of a certain form by means of an appropriate symbolic notation in order that the relevant features of the structure may be made plain and tested. In all this, we shall be concerned with the practical application of symbolic logic. But like any other science, logic is not studied primarily for reasons of utility. The development of logical techniques beyond what is necessary to provide a test of validity for forms of reasoning is an enterprise carried on for its own sake, like the development of pure mathematics. There are many branches of mathematics for which no practical application to problems of engineering, natural science, or statistics has yet been discovered. The same is true of the younger science of symbolic logic. Yet even here, branches of the subject which originally were developed for their intrinsic interest have been found capable of practical application and use in the most unlikely fields, from the constructing of calculating machines to the planning of electrical circuits. We shall be concerned in this book with the more elementary and traditionally practical parts of the subject. But it must be remembered that logic is now a rapidly growing subject and that many large and almost unexplored fields of knowledge lie beyond its present borders.

4. Inference and Implication. In Section 2 above, we considered some examples of simple formal arguments in order to introduce the notion of logical form. To take an instance, (1) was set out as follows:

(1) No capitalist societies are stable and some capitalist societies are democracies; therefore some democracies are not stable.

We could have expressed ourselves equally well thus:

(1*a*) If no capitalist societies are stable and some capitalist societies are democracies; then some democracies are not stable.

But there is a difference between (1) and (1*a*) and the difference is important. (1*a*) is a statement of logic to the effect that *if* certain conditions are fulfilled, then certain consequences will result. It says nothing as to whether or not the conditions referred to in the if-clause are, in fact, fulfilled. (1), on the other hand, is quite different. In the premisses of (1), certain *assertions* are made and as a logical consequence of these assertions a further assertion is made, namely, the fact stated in the conclusion. Thus, in order to be justified in asserting (1), we have to know not only that the logical form of the argument guarantees that the conclusion follows from the premisses but also that the premisses are *true*. And, as we have seen, this last condition is irrelevant to the logical question of validity. We are justified in asserting (1*a*), on the other hand, without prejudice to the question of the truth or falsity of the premisses. The most violent opponent of Marxism, for instance, could safely commit himself to (1*a*) whereas he certainly would not commit himself to (1). He could commit himself to (1*a*) because he would be saying merely: "*if* the premisses are true, *then* the conclusion is true".

To mark this important distinction, it is usual to call arguments like (1) *inferences* and statements in the form of (1*a*) *implications*. When we make an inference, we assume the truth of the premisses in asserting them; and as a consequence of the truth of the premisses and of the logical validity of the argument, we are entitled to assert the conclusion. But when we commit ourselves to an implication, we do not thereby commit ourselves to the truth of the premisses.

It would be strictly correct in a textbook of logic to set out all the examples as *implications* since we are concerned not with the material truth of our premisses but only with the logical validity of the form of expression which we are using. Nevertheless, it is probably more usual to express our examples as arguments, that is, in the form of an inference seeing that our everyday argumentation, being designed to establish the truth of the conclusion, must ordinarily be cast in this mould. We shall therefore set out our examples as inferences where this is more convenient and natural. And provided that the reader bears in mind the distinction between inference and implication, no confusion will result.

BIBLIOGRAPHICAL NOTE

CHAPTER I

There is no history of logic in English which takes account of the development of symbolic logic. Bochenski (3) and Lukasiewicz (21) are excellent on the early history of logic in its relation to modern logic. Boehner (4) relates some developments in medieval logic to modern symbolic logic but is not intended to be more than a sketch. The most satisfactory treatment of the classical syllogistic logic is in Keynes (17). An excellent simple account of the notion of logical form is given in Langer (19).

Note.—The numbers quoted in the bibliographical notes at the end of chapters refer to the bibliography at the end of the book.

CHAPTER II

THE CALCULUS OF PROPOSITIONS

1. Propositions and their Relations. The calculus of propositions (also known as the propositional calculus or the sentential calculus) is a basic part of logic and is usually taken as a starting point for the study of symbolic logic. We <u>shall understand by the term "proposition" any sentence which must be either true or false but which,</u> of course, cannot be *both* true *and* false. Thus "arsenic is poisonous", "$2 + 7 = 9$", "Napoleon was defeated at Waterloo" are propositions. And so are "arsenic is nutritious", "$2 + 7 = 10$", and "Napoleon was victorious at Waterloo". Thus we take "proposition" to mean what is meant by the grammatical term "indicative sentence". There are a number of philosophical difficulties which arise as soon as we try to make our concept of proposition more precise and explicit than this. But for the purposes of logic these difficulties may be ignored.

<u>In this branch of logic, we take propositions as our basic units.</u> In other words, we shall not be interested in breaking them down into their component parts as is necessary in testing the validity of certain types of arguments. Suppose, for example, that we are examining the validity of an argument of the following kind:

> (1) All dangerous trades should be highly paid.
> Mining is a dangerous trade.
> Therefore, mining should be highly paid.

This is, of course, a valid argument but its validity cannot be made plain unless we break down or analyse the propositions of which the argument is composed into their component terms. It is valid in virtue of certain relations

Def^t

16

between the terms "mining", "dangerous trades", and "trades which should be highly paid". We can express the form of the argument, abstracting from its subject-matter, if we write:

(2) All A's are B's.
X is an A.
Therefore, X is a B.

Now consider the following argument which is super-ficially similar to (1):

(3) If mining is a dangerous trade, then it should be highly paid.

Mining is a dangerous trade.
Therefore, mining should be highly paid.

The subject-matter of the two arguments is identical and the conclusion is the same in each case. Yet there is a very important difference between them. In (3), we do *not* have to break down the propositions making up the argument in order to demonstrate its validity. For the logical structure or form of the argument can be expressed as follows, if we replace the proposition "mining is a dangerous trade" by '*p*' and the proposition "mining should be highly paid" by '*q*':

(4) If *p*, then *q*.
p.
Therefore, *q*.

And this is clearly a valid form of argument, irrespective of the subject-matter of the propositions which '*p*' and '*q*' are made to represent. It is with arguments of the second type that we shall be concerned in our treatment of the calculus of propositions.

We shall not, however, be concerned with the subject-matter of propositions but only with the essential feature common to all propositions, namely, their capacity for truth or falsehood. It was given above as a defining character of a proposition that it must take one, and only one, of the two values "true" and "false". It is usual to call the truth or falsity of a proposition its *truth-value*. We shall therefore be interested in the propositional calculus, in propositions considered as bearing truth-values, and in the various ways in which these propositions may be combined and in the consequences of these combinations. This is vague at the moment but as we proceed it will become clearer.

We start then with the intuitive concept of "proposition" which we take from common-sense usage. We are also familiar from common-sense discourse with the notion that propositions may be combined in various ways and that they may be negated. For example, the propositions "the barometer is falling" and "there will be a storm" may be combined as follows:

(5) *If* the barometer is falling, *then* there will be a storm.

(6) *Either* the barometer is falling *or* there will be a storm.

(7) The barometer is falling *and* there will be a storm.

They may also be negated as follows:

(8) The barometer is *not* falling.

(9) There will *not* be a storm.

And it will be immediately obvious that the compound propositions (5) to (7) and the negated propositions (8) and (9) also satisfy the definition of "proposition" which was given above. That is to say, they are sentences which take one, and only one, of the two truth-values "true" and "false".

If now we neglect the *meaning* or *content* of these compounded and negated propositions, we can replace the original uncompounded and unnegated sentences by letters of the alphabet. We then obtain the following expressions:

(10) If p, then q.

(11) Either p or q.

(12) p and q.

(13) not-p.

(14) not-q.

It is with expressions of this kind, compounded in varying degrees of complexity, that we shall be concerned in the propositional calculus.

2. Truth-Functions. The notion of a *function* will be familiar from elementary mathematics. An expression is said to be a function of a given variable or variables, if the value of the expression is uniquely determined when the variable or variables take a determinate value. For example, if we have the expression:

$$y = 3x + 2$$

then y is a function of x, because its value is determined as soon as the variable x takes a value. Thus if x takes the value 0, the value of y is 2; if x takes the value 7, the value of y is 23; if x takes the value -4, then the value of y is -10; and so on. Likewise an expression such as:

$$z = 2x - 4y + 6$$

is a function of *two* variables x and y. And when their values are determined, the value of z is also determined. Thus, if x and y both take the value 1, the value of z is 4; if x is 3 and y is 4, then the value of z is -4; and so on.

We find that in logic we can usefully extend this notion of function in the following way. We have seen that every proposition takes one of the two values "true" or "false". And we have seen also that propositions which are compounded or negated as shown above are also either true or false. Moreover, *the truth-value of the compounded or negated proposition is uniquely determined by the truth-values of its original expressions*, just as the numerical value of a simple mathematical function is determined by the values taken by the variables occurring in the function.

Let us take as an example the compound sentence (1): "The sun is shining *and* the temperature is 70 degrees Fahrenheit". (1) will be true if, and only if, both its component sentences are true. If either or both of its component sentences are false, then (1) will itself be false. These facts may be expressed concisely in the following way: Let us represent the component sentences "the sun is shining" and "the temperature is 70 degrees Fahrenheit" by '*p*' and '*q*' respectively, seeing that we are concerned not with the *meanings* of the sentences in question but solely with their truth-values. Then we can represent the dependence of the truth-value of the compound sentence (1) on the truth-values of its component sentences as follows:

p	q	p and q
true	true	true
true	false	false
false	true	false
false	false	false

The compound sentence "*p* and *q*" is called a *truth-function* of its component sentences '*p*' and '*q*' because, when we know the truth-values of the component sentences, the truth-value of the compound sentence is thereby determined. And the tabular way of representing this dependence, set out above, is called a *truth-table*. It will, of course, be obvious that the truth-table given applies to *all* compound propositions in which two component propositions are joined by "and" and not only to sentence (1) which we took as our concrete example.

We can construct truth-tables to represent other truth-functions in a similar way. For example, the negation of any proposition is a truth-function of that proposition as shown in the following truth-table:

p	not-p
true	false
false	true

3. Basic Truth-Tables of the Propositional Calculus. We have seen that the basic material of the propositional calculus is of two kinds: (i) letters of the alphabet p, q, r, and so on (or sometimes p_1, p_2, p_3, and so on), stand for propositions. These letters, as used in the propositional calculus, are known as *propositional variables* because they stand indifferently for *any* proposition. (ii) Words like "not", "and", "or", and "if . . . then . . ." which link the propositional variables into truth-functional expressions, that is to say, compound expressions like "not-p or q", or "if p, then not-q" whose truth-values depend on the truth-values of their component propositions. These linking words are known as *logical constants*.

It is convenient (and conventional) to represent these logical constants by artificial symbols thus:

> For "not-p", we write '$\sim p$'.
> For "p and q", we write '$p \cdot q$'.
> For "p or q", we write '$p \vee q$'.
> For "if p, then q", we write '$p \supset q$'.

It is also convenient, in order to write our truth-tables concisely, to use the capital letter 'T' or the numeral '1' for "true" and the capital letter 'F' or the numeral '0' for "false". We can now go on to consider the basic truth-functions of the propositional calculus one by one, using this new notation.

The Contradictory Function.—If we negate any proposition, we obtain another proposition which is false if the original proposition is true and true if the original proposition is false. Thus, if the proposition "there are kangaroos in Australia" is true, its negation "there are no kangaroos in Australia", or "it is false that there are kangaroos in Australia", is false. Similarly, if the proposition "Nero was the first president of the United States" is false, then its negation "Nero was not the first president of the United States", or "it is false that Nero was the first president of the United States", is true. We can summarise these facts conveniently in a truth-table as follows:

p	$\sim p$
1	0
0	1

Thus when we prefix any proposition by the negation sign '$\sim$', we alter its truth-value from 1 to 0 or from 0 to 1. It follows that if we negate a negated proposition, we have the original proposition: to assert '$\sim \sim p$' is the same as to assert 'p'.

The Conjunctive Function.—This has already been discussed above in connection with sentence (1) of Section 2. The truth-table for the function can be set out as follows:

p	q	$p.q$
1	1	1
1	0	0
0	1	0
0	0	0

The Disjunctive Function.—A disjunctive truth-function of propositions is a compound proposition in which two (or more) propositions are joined into one by the word "or". Now the English word "or" is ambiguous and has at least two distinct meanings. Thus before we draw up the truth-table for the disjunctive function, we have to decide which meaning of the word we are going to adopt for the purpose of logic. If you are asked, "Will you have tea or coffee for breakfast?" the word "or" will be understood to preclude the answer "Both", although it is possible, if eccentric, to drink both at the same meal. On the other hand, if you are told "either John or Mary will meet you at the station", you would not be surprised or think that your informant had misled you if *both* John *and* Mary were at the station to meet you.

Thus "*p* or *q*" can have the exclusive sense of "either *p* or *q* but not both" or the inclusive sense of "either *p* or *q* or both". It has been found more convenient for the purposes of logic to adopt the second of these two meanings and, therefore, to interpret the word "or" in the *inclusive* sense. The truth-table for the disjunctive function is accordingly:

p	q	$p \vee q$
1	1	1
1	0	1
0	1	1
0	0	0

Thus the compound proposition '$p \vee q$' is true in every case *except* the case in which *both* the component propositions are false.

The Implicative Function.—Of the logical constants referred to above, one remains to be discussed. The implicative function "if *p*, then *q*" is a very important function in logic but the task of constructing a truth-table for it and thus demonstrating it to be a truth-function of its component propositions is not quite so simple as in the previous cases. The reason for this is that our ordinary colloquial use of the phrase "if . . . then" in English is not obviously related to the truth-values of the propositions which are linked by the phrase. In the case of the three previous functions, on the other hand, the everyday use of the English words "not", "and", and "or" is fairly obviously truth-functional. Thus we can construct the truth-tables for these logical constants by referring to the everyday meanings of the corresponding English words. But how are we to construct the truth-table for the implicative function without arbitrarily distorting the usual meaning of the phrase "if . . . then"?

Fortunately, we are able to do so by translating the logical constant "if . . . then" into two of the logical constants whose truth-tables we have already been able to construct. The meaning of the expression "if p, then q" is substantially equivalent to that of the expression "either not-p or q". Thus, the sentences:

(1) If the price of gold rises, inflation will increase;

(2) If America attacks Russia, Europe will be ruined;

can be expressed respectively without any change of meaning as:

(3) Either the price of gold will not rise or inflation will increase;

(4) Either America will not attack Russia or Europe will be ruined.

The difference between the two forms of expression is merely rhetorical, the second form being somewhat less usual than the first.

We are therefore in a position to construct the truth-table for the implicative function indirectly, by constructing the table for the disjunction of a negated proposition and an unnegated proposition. We can do this in the following way:

p	$\sim p$	q	$\sim p \vee q$
1	0	1	1
1	0	0	0
0	1	1	1
0	1	0	1

Thus the truth-table for '$p \supset q$' is as follows:

p	q	$p \supset q$
1	1	1
1	0	0
0	1	1
0	0	1

It will be observed that this use of "if-then" defined as a truth-function of the antecedent proposition 'p' and the consequent 'q' is a good deal wider than that which is current in idiomatic English. The most common use of implicative sentences in ordinary language is to state causal or other "necessary" connections between one fact and another, as, for example, when I say "if the temperature of a piece of iron is increased, then its volume is increased". Here we mean that the truth of the consequent follows from or is guaranteed by the truth of the antecedent. This use corresponds, so far as the truth-values of the component propositions and the resulting compound proposition are concerned, to the first row of the truth-table set out above. And there is an idiomatic use of implicative sentences which corresponds to the *last* row of the table. If a teacher says of a student "if he passes that examination, I'll eat my hat", he intends to imply that *both* the antecedent of the implication and the consequent are false, even though the implication itself is asserted as true. This is, of course, nothing more than a rhetorical way of expressing a forceful denial of the antecedent.

Nevertheless, in spite of these analogies between the truth-functional interpretation of "if-then" sentences and our ordinary conversational use of such sentences, the truth-table for the logical constant '$\supset$' does appear to involve paradoxes. It follows, for example, from this definition of the logical constant "if-then" that a true proposition is implied by *any* proposition, true or false, and that a false proposition *implies* any proposition, true or false. It does, of course, seem wildly paradoxical to maintain that the following are examples of true implications:

(5) If Brutus killed Caesar, then there are lions in Africa.

(6) If Caesar killed Brutus, then there are lions in Africa.

(7) If Nero was a Christian saint, then $5 + 7 = 16$.

These implications seem to common sense to be neither true nor false but rather to be nonsensical because the ordinary use of "if-then" in linking sentences into implications presupposes that it is the *meanings* of the sentences so linked (and not their truth-values) which determine whether the implication is true or false. This is true; but it is not a good reason for rejecting a truth-functional approach to the logic of propositions. It is perhaps a good reason for not using the word "implication" of "if-then" sentences when they are interpreted in a truth-functional sense. And it is, in fact, now more usual to call this relation "*material implication*" to distinguish it from the ordinary conversational use of "if-then". Nevertheless, the truth-functional interpretation of "if-then" is a perfectly satisfactory one for logic. It will be seen that the apparent paradoxes arise only because the truth-functional sense is *wider* than the conversational sense. But being wider, it includes it. Moreover, it works in practice. And this, for our purposes, is a sufficient justification of the novelty of the usage. We shall, therefore, take the truth-table given above as a *definition* of the way in which the logical constant ' $\supset$ ' is to operate in the propositional calculus.

4. Relations between Truth-Functions. We have seen that it is possible to define the logical constant of the implicative function ' $\supset$ ' in terms of ' $\sim$ ' and 'v'. It is also possible to define both '∨' and '.' in terms of other logical constants. But '∼' has to be taken as a primitive idea which we accept as undefinable in terms of any of the other constants so far introduced. For the purposes of the propositional calculus, we may take the truth-table of each of the truth-functions set out above as a *definition* of that function and as a rule for the use of the logical constant occurring in the function. Thus:

p	q	$p \supset q$
1	1	1
1	0	0
0	1	1
0	0	1

is, for our purposes, a definition of the implicative function and a rule for the use of ' $\supset$ ' in the calculus of propositions.

Since the truth-table of a given function is a definition of that function, any other function having the same truth-table will be equivalent to it and interchangeable with it for all logical purposes. Thus we saw that ' $\sim p \vee q$ ' is equivalent to ' $p \supset q$ ' in having the same truth-table. It can therefore be regarded as another way of defining the implicative function, though here the definition is of another kind, being stated in terms of other logical constants and not in terms of truth-values.

Similarly, ' $p \supset q$ ' can be expressed in terms of ' $\sim$ ' and ' . ' as: ' $\sim (p . \sim q)$ '. For example, "if this metal is heated, it will expand" is the same as "it is false that this metal will be heated and it will not expand". The truth-table is as follows:

p	q	$\sim q$	$\sim (p . \sim q)$
1	1	0	1
1	0	1	0
0	1	0	1
0	0	1	1

Here the final column of the table is identical with the final column of the table for '$p \supset q$'. Thus the expressions '$p \supset q$', '$\sim p \vee q$', and '$\sim (p . \sim q)$' are logically equivalent and may, for all logical purposes, be substituted one for another.

The logical constant ' . ' may be defined in terms of '$\sim$' and '$\vee$', and, therefore, also in terms of '$\sim$' and '$\supset$' as follows. (We shall use the expression '$=_{df}$' to mean "is equivalent to by definition".)

$$p . q =_{df} \sim (\sim p \vee \sim q) =_{df} \sim (p \supset \sim q).$$

For example, the proposition "he is both lazy and stupid" means the same as "it is false that either he is not lazy or he is not stupid" and "it is false that if he is lazy then he is not stupid". The constant '$\vee$' may similarly be defined in terms of '$\sim$' and ' . ', and of '$\sim$' and '$\supset$':

$$p \vee q =_{df} \sim (\sim p . \sim q) =_{df} \sim p \supset q.$$

Thus the proposition "this letter is either a forgery or important evidence" is logically equivalent to "it is false that this letter is both not a forgery and not important evidence" and to "if this letter is not a forgery, then it is important evidence".

Summarising, we have:

(1) $p \supset q =_{df} \sim p \vee q =_{df} \sim (p . \sim q)$.

(2) $p . q =_{df} \sim (\sim p \vee \sim q) =_{df} \sim (p \supset \sim q)$.

(3) $p \vee q =_{df} \sim (\sim p . \sim q) =_{df} \sim p \supset q$.

It must be remembered that, in each case, what we mean by saying that these expressions are equivalent is that they have the same truth-table. This was shown above for the equivalences of (1). The reader should verify the other equivalences by constructing the appropriate truth-tables.

5. Further Logical Constants. It will be seen from what has been said above about logical constants controlling two variables, such as "and" or "if-then", that they are defined by a characteristic truth-table consisting of four digits, each of which is either 1 or 0. Thus the characteristic truth-table for the conjunctive function is 1000 (writing the column horizontally for convenience) and the characteristic truth-table for the implicative function is 1011. These numbers are called the truth-table numbers or matrix-numbers of the truth-function in question. Thus the matrix-number of the disjunctive function is 1110.

It will also be obvious from what has been said that any two functions which have the same matrix-number such as '$p \supset q$' and '$\sim p \lor q$' are, for logical purposes, equivalent and interchangeable. The possibility of representing functions by numbers in this way raises the question: how many possible *different* functions of two variables are there? In other words, in how many different ways may four places be filled by the numbers 1 and 0? Clearly, the answer is $2 \times 2 \times 2 \times 2$, that is 2^4 or 16 different ways.

Now of these sixteen possible functions, we have considered only three, namely, 1000, 1011, and 1110. How many of the others do we need to take account of? Not all of them are logically interesting, but there are several others which are worth examining. We shall look at three of them.

The Equivalence Function.—Two propositions are said to be *equivalent*, or more commonly, *materially equivalent*, when they have the same truth-value. It is sometimes convenient in the propositional calculus to have a symbolic method of representing this equivalence and it is ordinarily expressed by the symbol '$\equiv$'. Thus '$p \equiv q$' is true if 'p' and 'q' have the same truth-value. Otherwise it is false. The truth-table is therefore as follows:

p	q	$p \equiv q$
1	1	1
1	0	0
0	1	0
0	0	1

Thus the matrix-number characterising the equivalence function is 1001.

There is no very common expression in English corresponding to the equivalence function. The only idiomatic way of expressing this function in English seems to be by the use of the phrase "if and only if". The proposition "he will pass if, and only if he works hard" is true if the component propositions "he will pass" and "he will work hard" are both true *and also* if they are both false. It is false if the first is false and the second true or if the first is true and the second false. Moreover, it has the same meaning as the *conjunction* of the two implications "if he works hard, then he will pass" and "if he passes, then he will work hard". Thus '$p \equiv q$' is equivalent to the conjunctive function '$p \supset q . q \supset p$'. And if we construct the truth-table for the latter function, we shall see that it is identical with the truth-table for '$p \equiv q$' set out above.

p	q	$p \supset q$	$q \supset p$	$p \supset q . q \supset p$
1	1	1	1	1
1	0	0	1	0
0	1	1	0	0
0	0	1	1	1

It should be noted that just as in the case of the implicative function we arrive at apparently paradoxical results by neglecting the *meanings* of the propositions with which we are dealing and attending only to their *truth-values*, so we arrive at similarly paradoxical cases of the equivalence function. This is not surprising, seeing that equivalence can be defined in terms of a conjunction of implicative functions. Thus the proposition "Nero was a Roman emperor" is equivalent to the proposition "all men are mortal", because both are true. And the proposition "the earth is flat" is equivalent to the proposition "Russia invaded Germany in 1941", since both are false. In fact, *any* true proposition is equivalent to *any* other true proposition (or to itself); and *any* false proposition is equivalent to *any* other false proposition (or to itself). To mitigate the strangeness of this use of the word "equivalent" it is common to translate the expression '$p \equiv q$' as "p is *materially equivalent* to q".

The strangeness of this usage need not trouble us, for we shall find, as in the case of the implicative function, that the definition of the function, given by its truth-table, works quite satisfactorily. Logical rules have, after all, to be perfectly general in their application and need not be restricted to the notions conveyed by ordinary language, provided that they do cover those notions. And the use of '$\equiv$' outlined above does cover the ordinary meaning of "if and only if". But it legislates for other cases as well which in ordinary language have no conventional mode of expression.

The Alternative Function.—We decided above that the word "or" has two meanings in English and that for the purposes of the basic logical constants we selected the *inclusive* sense of the word. That is to say, '$p \lor q$' was to be read as "either p or q and possibly both are true". But it is easy, on the basis of the constants already introduced, to define the exclusive "or" and to construct its truth-table. Let us use the symbol '$\land$' for the exclusive "or". Then the truth-table will be:

p	q	$p \land q$
1	1	0
1	0	1
0	1	1
0	0	0

And this is also the truth-table for '$((p \lor q) . \sim (p.q))$' as the reader may easily verify for himself. Thus:

$$p \land q =_{df} ((p \lor q) . \sim (p.q)) =_{df} ((p \lor q) . (\sim p \lor \sim q)).$$

The Stroke Function.—We introduced as basic logical constants '$\sim$', '$\vee$', '$.$', and '$\supset$'. And we have defined '$\equiv$' and '$\wedge$' in terms of these. We have seen too that '$\vee$', '$.$', and '$\supset$' are definable in terms of each other with the help of the primitive constant '$\sim$'. The fact that logical constants are interdefinable in this way leads us to ask "How many of these constants are really indispensable for building up our calculus of propositions?". From the results we have already arrived at, we have seen that we can dispense with all but two. For '$\supset$' and '$.$' can be defined in terms of '$\sim$' and '$\vee$', and '$\vee$' can be defined in terms of '$\sim$' and '$.$' or, alternatively, in terms of '$\sim$' and '$\supset$'. Can the number of indispensable constants be reduced still further? The answer is that we can dispense with all logical constants save one. (There are two ways in which this can be done.) The function which we shall use for this purpose is known as the *stroke-function* and it is defined as follows: 'p/q' is to be read "at least one of p and q is false". The truth-table will be:

p	q	p/q
1	1	0
1	0	1
0	1	1
0	0	1

It is clear that this function, being read as "at least one of p and q is false" is equivalent to '$\sim p \vee \sim q$'.

Let us now see how the logical constants which we have taken as basic can be defined in terms of the stroke-function.

(*a*) $\sim p =_{df} p/p$.

For if either 'p' is false or 'p' is false, then obviously 'p' is false. A consideration of the truth-tables will make the identity clear.

p	$\sim p$		p	p	p/p
1	0		1	1	0
0	1		0	0	1

(b) $p.q =_{df} (p/q)/(p/q)$.

Since 'p/p' is equivalent to '$\sim p$', '$(p/q)/(p/q)$' is equivalent to '$\sim (p/q)$'. And since '(p/q)' means "at least one of p and q is false", '$\sim (p/q)$' means "it is false that at least one of p and q is false" or "both p and q are true", i.e. '$(p.q)$'.

(c) $p \vee q =_{df} (p/p)/(q/q)$.

Since '(p/p)' is equivalent to '$\sim p$', the right-hand side of this definition may be read '$\sim p/\sim q$', which reads "either not-p or not-q is false". And this, in turn, may be read as "either p or q is true", i.e. '$(p \vee q)$'.

(d) $p \supset q =_{df} p/(q/q)$.

Here the right-hand side of the definition is equivalent to '$p/\sim q$', which can be read as "either p is false or not-q is false" or "either p is false or q is true", i.e. '$\sim p \vee q$', which we have already seen to be equivalent to '$p \supset q$'.

Thus it is clearly possible to write all the expressions of the propositional calculus in terms of propositional variables $p, q, r \ldots$ and a single logical constant, the stroke. But what we gain in economy of basic concepts by the use of the stroke as our single constant, we lose in psychological obviousness. Clearly,

$$(\sim p.q) \supset q$$

is much more readily understood than:

$$(((p/p)/q)/((p/p)/q))/(q/q).$$

But these expressions are equivalent, as the reader may verify by applying the definitions given above to transform one expression into the other or by constructing the truth-tables.

CHAPTER III

THE CALCULUS OF PROPOSITIONS
(*continued*)

1. The Truth-Table Method of Testing the Validity of Arguments. So far we have been using truth-tables merely as a convenient device for explaining the notion of truth-functional dependence. We shall now proceed to use them in what will seem to most readers to be a more practical and interesting way, namely, as a test of the validity of arguments. But before we can apply them in this way, there are several rules of construction and procedure which have to be considered. We have been concerned so far with very simple functions of one or two variables. But we have to be prepared to deal with arguments of considerable complexity involving truth-functional expressions of several variables. Our procedure, up to now, has taken for granted, as being obvious in simple cases, several rules which have to be made quite explicit before we proceed to deal with cases of greater complexity.

Let us first consider the question of the number of propositional variables involved in truth-functional expressions. The truth-table for the contradictory function, given above, deals with the truth-values of one propositional variable 'p', and has two rows and two columns. The two rows exhaust the possible combinations of truth-values which can be assigned to the variable 'p' and its negation. And of the two columns, the first contains the possible truth-values of 'p' and the second the corresponding values of 'not-p'. Thus:

p	$\sim p$
1	0
0	1

When we turn to a truth-function of two variables '*p*' and '*q*', the position is more complex. Let us take as an example the disjunctive function:

p	*q*	*p* V *q*
1	1	1
1	0	1
0	1	1
0	0	0

Here we have four rows and three columns. It will be seen that the four rows of the columns beneath the variable '*p*' set out the truth-values in the order 1100 and the column beneath '*q*' sets out the truth-values of '*q*' in the order 1010. They are set down in this way so that the four possible combinations of the truth-values of '*p*' and '*q*', namely, 11, 10, 01, and 00 are all given. It will be seen later why it is essential that *all* the possible combinations of the truth-values of the propositional variables should be given. Thus a truth-table of one variable sets down the truth-values of that variable in the order 10. And a truth-table of two variables sets down the truth-values of the first variable in the order 1100 and the truth-values of the second variable in the order 1010.

Now let us suppose that we have to construct a truth-table for a propositional expression containing three variables, say:

$$(p \lor r) \supset (q \lor r).$$

We have seen that a function of one variable has 2^1 or two truth-possibilities and a function of two variables has 2^2 or four truth-possibilities. We need now to know how many truth-possibilities there are for a function of three variables like the one given above. Clearly there will be 2^3 or eight. For the third variable has two truth-possibilities, 1 and 0, and each of these has to be combined with the four truth-possibilities of the first two variables. We shall therefore need eight rows in the truth-table.

We now have to decide how the truth-values are to be set down in order to cover all the eight truth-possibilities. It will be seen that the following order will satisfy this requirement (though it is not, of course, the only possible one):

p	q	r
1	1	1
1	1	0
1	0	1
1	0	0
0	1	1
0	1	0
0	0	1
0	0	0

We can now summarise what has been said above and generalise it for truth-functions of any number of variables in the following two rules:

(1) A truth-function of n variables needs 2^n rows to provide for all its truth-possibilities.

(2) The order of arrangement in columns of the truth-values of each of the variables is as follows: where n is the total number of variables, the column under the mth variable contains 2^{m-1} sets of 2^{n-m} 1's followed by 2^{n-m} 0's.

These rules may be exemplified as follows:

Case 1.—Suppose we have a function of two variables. Then (i) there will be 2^2 or four rows. (ii) The column under the *first* variable will consist of 2^{1-1} or 2^0, that is, one set of 2^{2-1} or two 1's followed by the same number of 0's, thus: 1100.

Case 2.—Suppose that we have a function of four variables. Then (i) there will be 2^4 or sixteen rows in the truth-table. (ii) If we construct the column under the third variable, we shall have 2^{3-1} or four sets of 2^{4-3} or two 1's followed by the same number of 0's, thus:

$$1100110011001100.$$

Case 3.—Let us suppose a function of *five* variables. Then (i) there will be 2^5 or thirty-two rows in the truth-table. (ii) If we wish to construct the column under, say, the third variable, we shall have 2^{3-1} or four sets of 2^{5-3} or four 1's followed by the same number of 0's, thus:

$$11110000111100001111000011110000.$$

It will be obvious that the truth-tables become cumbrous and unwieldy where the truth-functional expression with which we are dealing contains more than four or five propositional variables. Fortunately there are shorter methods which, as we shall see, can be applied where the full truth-tables are too clumsy to be used conveniently.

2. Logical Punctuation and the Scope of Constants. Owing to the comparative simplicity of the expressions with which we have so far been dealing and the small number of variables involved, we have been able to take for granted certain rules about the grouping and punctuation of logical expressions. These rules must now be made explicit before we can go on to deal with more complex expressions. Consider the following propositions:

(1) It is false that he is ambitious and hard-working.

(2) If he is ambitious, then if he is offered the job, he will take it.

(3) The Government will fall, or they will get a vote of confidence and stay in power.

Suppose that we put these propositions into logical notation respectively as follows:

(4) $\sim p.q.$

(5) $p \supset q \supset r.$

(6) $p \vee q.r.$

These translations into the symbolism of the propositional calculus are clearly inadequate as they stand because they are ambiguous. We do not know, without referring back to our original proposition (1), whether (4) shall be read as "p is false and q is true" or "it is false that p and q are true". Moreover, (5) could be read either as "if p, then if q then r", or as "if, if p then q, then r". Again, we do not know without referring back to the original proposition (2) which of these two readings is correct. And similarly, (6) may be read either as "either p or q is true and r is true" or as "either p is true or q and r are both true".

When we are using everyday English, such ambiguities can easily be overcome. But the logical language, which we have so far at our disposal, is not rich enough to afford us any means of avoiding them. We must therefore introduce rules which will provide such a means.

Let us define the _scope_ of a logical constant as those parts of a truth-functional expression which are controlled by the constant. Thus the proposition "it is false that he is both ambitious and hardworking" or "he is not both ambitious and hardworking" [proposition (1) above] is translated into logical notation as:

$$\sim (p.q)$$

Here the scope of the negation sign '$\sim$' is the whole of the rest of the function. Contrast this with: "he is not ambitious but he is hardworking". We translate this as:

$$(\sim p).q.$$

And here the scope of the constant '$\sim$' is confined to 'p'

by the device of confining this part of the expression in brackets.

Whereas the constant '∼' controls, or operates over, only the expression (or part of the expression) which *follows* it, the other constants which have been introduced control or operate over the expression (or part of the expression) both preceding and following. For instance, in '$p \vee q$', the scope of '∨' is both 'p' and 'q'. And in '$p \vee (q.r)$' the scope of '∨' is both 'p' and '$(q.r)$', whereas in '$(p \vee q).r$' the scope of '∨' is confined to 'p' and 'q'. We shall call these *binary constants*.

We have therefore to introduce brackets into the symbolism of the propositional calculus in order to make explicit the scope of the logical constants which we are using, in cases where their scope would otherwise be ambiguous. The following rules for the use of brackets will suffice for our present purposes.

RP 1.—The scope of '∼' is confined to the propositional variable immediately succeeding it, except where '∼' is followed by a left-hand bracket '('. In this case, the scope of '∼' will extend to the *corresponding* right-hand bracket.

EXAMPLE 1.—In '$\sim p.q$', the scope of '∼' is 'p'.

EXAMPLE 2.—In '$\sim (p.(q \supset r) \vee s)$', the scope of '∼' is the whole expression.

EXAMPLE 3.—In '$\sim (p.q) \vee (r \supset s)$', the scope of '∼' is '$(p.q)$'.

RP 2.—If a binary constant is flanked by a propositional variable, the scope of the constant *on that side* is confined to the propositional variable. If a binary constant is flanked by a bracket, the scope of the constant extends to the *corresponding* bracket.

EXAMPLE 1.—In '$p \supset (q \vee r)$', the scope of the ' $\supset$ ' is the whole expression, i.e. 'p' and '$(q \vee r)$'.

EXAMPLE 2.—In the expression

$$`((p \supset q) \supset r) \supset ((r \supset p) \supset (s \supset p))`$$

the scope of the first ' $\supset$ ' is 'p' and 'q'; the scope of the second ' $\supset$ ' is '$(p \supset q)$' and 'r'; the scope of the third ' $\supset$ ' is the whole expression; and so on.

3. The Construction and Application of Truth-Tables.
Let us take as an example of a simple argument falling within the scope of the propositional calculus:

If Jones is innocent, part of the evidence is forged. But no part of the evidence is forged. Therefore, Jones is not innocent.

Here we have two premisses and a conclusion, the first premiss being an implication and the second premiss being the negation of the consequent of the first premiss. The conclusion is then the negation of the antecedent of the first premiss. The word "therefore" which precedes the conclusion indicates that the premisses taken together are asserted to *imply* the conclusion, or, in other words, that *if* the premisses are jointly asserted, then the conclusion follows. Let us therefore put for the proposition "Jones is innocent" the propositional variable 'p' and for the proposition "part of the evidence is forged" the variable 'q'. We can then represent the form of the argument in the notation of the propositional calculus as follows:

$$((p \supset q) . \sim q) \supset \sim p.$$

Let us now draw up a truth-table for this compound expression. Hitherto, in constructing truth-tables, we have drawn up the truth-values of the variables, in separate columns, to the left of the truth-table for the function under consideration, as follows:

p	q	$p \supset q$
1	1	1
1	0	0
0	1	1
0	0	1

This method is the clearest for elementary exposition. But it is more concise, and for practical applications more convenient, to draw up the table as follows:

$p \supset q$
1 1 1
1 0 0
0 1 1
0 1 0

so that the truth-table for the whole expression which is the scope of the logical constant is written directly beneath the constant in its position between the two variables. We shall adopt this practice in future.

Let us now construct the table for the truth-functional expression under consideration:

$$((p \supset q) . \sim q) \supset \sim p.$$

First of all, construct the columns of truth-values for the individual propositional variables from left to right, thus:

1	2	3	4
$((p$	$\supset q)$	$. \sim q)$	$\supset \sim p$
1	1	1	1
1	0	0	1
0	1	1	0
0	0	0	0

(The numbers above the propositional variables indicate the order in which the columns are to be completed.)

Next, construct the truth-tables, from left to right, of the constants of narrowest scope. (In this case, the first ' ⊃ ' and the two negation signs.)

1 5 2	6 3	7 4
$((p \supset q)$	$. \sim q)$	$\supset \sim p$

1 1 1	0 1	0 1
1 0 0	1 0	0 1
0 1 1	0 1	1 0
0 1 0	1 0	1 0

Next, construct the truth-table for the remaining constants, working from those of narrower scope to those of wider scope. The final table will read:

1 5 2	8	6 3	9	7 4
$((p \supset q)$		$. \sim q)$	$\supset$	$\sim p$

1 1 1	0	0 1	1	0 1
1 0 0	0	1 0	1	0 1
0 1 1	0	0 1	1	1 0
0 1 0	1	1 0	1	1 0

In step number 8, we form the table for the *conjunction* of '$(p \supset q)$' and '$\sim q$'. And finally, in step number 9, we complete the table by constructing the table for the constant of widest scope, the ' ⊃ ' standing between '$((p \supset q). \sim q)$' on the left and '$\sim p$' on the right. And to form the column, we apply the rule for the constant ' ⊃ ' taking column 8 as the antecedent and column 7 as the consequent.

It will be observed that the main column of the truth-table, that is the column beneath the constant of widest scope, contains only 1's. In other words, the expression is shown to be true for all the possible truth-combinations of the variables. And this means that the expression is *valid* or *logically true* or a *tautology*. (The terms italicised may be taken as synonymous.) Thus we have a method for testing the validity of arguments which can be expressed as implications in the notation of the propositional calculus. We construct the truth-table of such expressions and if the main column, that is the column beneath the constant of widest scope, contains only 1's, the argument is valid. But if there is at least one 0 in the main column, then the argument is *invalid*.

Suppose that, instead of the argument which we took as an example above, we take the following:

If Jones is innocent, then part of the evidence is forged. But Jones is not innocent. Therefore part of the evidence is not forged.

Putting this argument into the notation of the propositional calculus as before, we have:

$$((p \supset q) . \sim p) \supset \sim q.$$

Now let us construct the truth-table for this expression. We have:

((p	⊃	q)	.	~p)	⊃	~q
1	1	1	0	0 1	1	0 1
1	0	0	0	0 1	1	1 0
0	1	1	1	1 0	0	0 1
0	1	0	1	1 0	1	1 0

Here we see that the column beneath the main constant does *not* consist only of 1's. It has a 0 in the third row, thus showing that the expression is not true for all the truth-possibilities of its variables. Its value is 0 in the case where *p* takes the value 0 and *q* takes the value 1, that is in the third row.

Where the expression is complicated by the presence of three or four or even more propositional variables, the procedure is the same as in the examples taken above. Consider the following example:

$((p$	$\supset$	$q)$	$.$	$(\sim r \supset \sim q)) \supset (p \supset r)$

1	1	1	1	0	1	1	0	1	1	1	1	1
1	1	1	0	1	0	0	0	1	1	1	0	0
1	0	0	0	0	1	1	1	0	1	1	1	1
1	0	0	0	1	0	1	1	0	1	1	0	0
0	1	1	1	0	1	1	0	1	1	0	1	1
0	1	1	0	1	0	0	0	1	1	0	1	0
0	1	0	1	0	1	1	1	0	1	0	1	1
0	1	0	1	1	0	1	1	0	1	0	1	0

Thus we have, in the truth-table, an automatic method of deciding in the case of any expression in the propositional calculus whether or not it is *logically true* or *tautological*. And this means, if the expression is the form of an argument, that we have a means of deciding whether any argument which falls within the scope of the propositional calculus is valid or not.

4. An Indirect Method of Truth-Table Decision. We have seen that the number of rows necessary in a truth-table increases in geometrical progression as the number of variables increases, and that this results in expressions of five or more variables becoming awkward to manage by the methods outlined above. There is, however, a shorter and indirect method of testing validity which rests on the principles governing the construction of truth-tables. We have seen that the truth-table of a valid expression contains in the column under the main constant (that is, under the constant of widest scope) only the number 1. If now we make the hypothesis that such an expression has a 0 in the main column of its table and examine the consequences of this hypothesis, we shall find that these consequences are inconsistent with the basic rules for the construction of truth-tables.

Let us consider the expression:

$$`((p \supset q) . \sim q) \supset \sim p',$$

which was truth-tabled above. Write the expression with a 0 beneath the constant of widest scope and proceed to fill in the consequential truth-values in accordance with the rules.

Step 1.
$$((p \supset q) . \sim q) \supset \sim p$$

| | 1 | 0 0 |
| | 1 | 1 |

(The second row of numbers beneath the truth-values is to enumerate the steps of the procedure, so that it can be checked on completion.) We put 1 beneath the main constant of the antecedent and 0 beneath the constant of the consequent as this assignment of values follows from the assumption that the whole expression takes the value 0. Proceeding similarly we have:

Step 2.
$$((p \supset q) . \sim q) \supset \sim p$$

| 1 | 1 1 | 0 0 |
| 2 | 1 2 | 1 |

Step 3.
$$((p \supset q) . \sim q) \supset \sim p$$

| 1 | 1 1 0 0 | 0 1 |
| 2 | 1 2 3 | 1 3 |

Step 4.
$$((p \supset q) . \sim q) \supset \sim p$$

| 1 1 0 | 1 1 0 0 | 0 1 |
| 4 2 4 | 1 2 3 | 1 3 |

In this final step we fill in the values of 'p' and 'q' derived from the preceding steps and find that we have the expression '$(p \supset q)$' taking the value 1, while 'p' takes the value 1 and 'q' takes the value 0. And reference to the truth-table prescribing the truth-functional use of '$\supset$' shows that this is not permitted. Thus the assumption that 0 occurs in the main column of the table has led to a contradiction of the basic rules of the truth-table procedure. Hence *no* 0 can occur in the main column; and therefore the expression is valid.

This method may be seen to be similar to the *reductio ad absurdum* type of proof used in geometry. The consequences of a certain assumption lead to an untenable conclusion. Thus the assumption (in this case, the assumption that the value 0 occurs in the main column) is shown to be false.

On the other hand, if the assumption that the main column of the truth-table contains a 0 does *not* lead to a violation of the rules, then the main column *does* contain a 0 and the expression is invalid. For example:

$$((p \supset q) . \sim p) \supset \sim q$$

0	1	1	1 1 0	0 0 1
5	2	6	1 2 3	1 4

Here the combinations of truth-values are in accordance with the basic rules of the truth-table method. Thus our assumption that a 0 occurs in the main column leads to no violation of the rules and the expression is therefore *invalid*.

As an example of the indirect method applied to an expression of several variables, let us consider the following:

$$((p \supset q) \supset r) \supset ((r \supset p) \supset (s \supset p))$$

0 0	1 0 0	0 1 0 0	1 0 0
4 7	1 6	5 2 4 1	3 2 3

In this example, the expression '$(p \supset q)$' takes the value 0 while 'p' also takes the value 0. And this is impossible by the truth-table for the implicative function. Thus the expression is a valid one. (Notice that there is no need to determine the value of 'q'. The result would be the same whether 'q' takes the value 0 or 1.)

There are occasional cases in which the proof cannot be completed in a single line. For example, if we cannot avoid placing '1' under '∨' or '$\supset$' or '0' under '.' and have to proceed from that point, we shall need a separate line for each of the alternatives. Such cases are not common and are in any event more concise than a complete truth-table.

5. The Classification of Propositions. Any truthfunctional expression may be truth-tabled and classified into one of three types in accordance with the character of its truth-table, or, more properly, in accordance with the character of its matrix-number. If the matrix-number, *i.e.* the sequence of digits in the main column of its truth-table contains only 1's, the expression is *valid* or *logically true* or a *tautology.* (We may regard these terms as synonymous in this context.) If the matrix-number contains only 0's, then the expression is *logically false* or *contradictory* or *contravalid.* But if, as will be the case with most expressions, the main column contains both 1's and 0's, the expression is *contingent*, its truth or falsity depending upon a particular combination of truth-values of the variables, and being true for certain truth-possibilities and false for others. For example:

(a)

$$(p \supset q) \equiv (\sim q \supset \sim p)$$

1	1	1	1	0	1	1	0	1
1	0	0	1	1	0	0	0	1
0	1	1	1	0	1	1	1	0
0	1	0	1	1	0	1	1	0

(b)

$$(p \supset q) \cdot (p \cdot \sim q)$$

1	1	1	0	1	0	0	1
1	0	0	0	1	1	1	0
0	1	1	0	0	0	0	1
0	1	0	0	0	0	1	0

(c)

(	p	⊃	q	)	⊃	(q	V	r	)
	1	1	1		1	1	1	1	
	1	1	1		1	1	1	0	
	1	0	0		1	0	1	1	
	1	0	0		1	0	0	0	
	0	1	1		1	1	1	1	
	0	1	1		1	1	1	0	
	0	1	0		1	0	1	1	
	0	1	0		0	0	0	0	

It will be seen that of the expressions tabled above (a) is logically true, (b) logically false, and (c) is contingent. In the case of (c), the truth-value of the expression comes out as 0 for the single case where 'p', 'q', and 'r' all take the value 0.

Two important points follow from this classification:

(i) Every logically false or contravalid expression is the negation of a logically true or tautologous expression and vice versa.

(ii) Every logically true expression is logically equivalent to every other logically true expression; and similarly, every contravalid expression is equivalent to every other contravalid expression.

6. Reference Formulae. It will be useful to list here for reference some of the most important of the logically true expressions.

RF 1: $\sim(p.\sim p)$.—This is the Law of Non-Contradiction* of the traditional logic applied to propositions. It states that no proposition can be both true and false.

RF 2: $(p \vee \sim p)$.—This is the Law of the Excluded Middle* of the traditional logic applied to propositions. It states that every proposition must be either true or false.

* See footnote on following page.

RF 3: $(p \supset p)$.—This is the Law of Identity* of the traditional logic applied to propositions. It states that every proposition implies itself. It will be seen that these three laws, RF 1-3, can be transformed one into the other by applying the rules given in Section 4 above for the translation of one binary constant into '$\sim$' and another binary constant.

RF 4: $(p.q) \supset p$.

RF 5: $(p.q) \supset q$.

RF 4 and 5 state that a conjunction implies either of the propositions conjoined.

RF 6: $p \supset (p \vee q)$.—If a proposition is true, then *any disjunction* is true of which the proposition is a member.

RF 7: $\sim\sim p \equiv p$.—The effect of doubling the negation sign is to cancel it. In other words, to deny a negated proposition is equivalent to affirming the proposition.

RF 8: $(p.q) \equiv (q.p)$.

RF 9: $(p \vee q) \equiv (q \vee p)$.

RF 8 and 9 are the commutative laws for conjunction and disjunction respectively. They express the fact that the *order* of the functions forming the scope of '.' and '$\vee$' is immaterial. Notice that the commutative law does *not* apply to the constant '$\supset$'.

RF 10: $(p.(q.r)) \equiv ((p.q).r)$.

RF 11: $(p \vee (q \vee r)) \equiv ((p \vee q) \vee r)$.

RF 10 and 11 are the associative laws for conjunction and disjunction respectively. They express the fact that the grouping of expressions containing only '.' as a constant (or '$\vee$' as a constant) is immaterial to the validity

* The attribution of these titles to propositional formulae is strictly speaking incorrect. It is, however, not unusual in textbooks of symbolic logic, and we therefore retain it here.

of the expression. Notice again that the associative law does not apply to the constant '$\supset$'.

RF 12: $(p.(q \lor r)) \equiv (p.q) \lor (p.r).$

RF 13: $(p \lor (q.r)) \equiv (p \lor q).(p \lor r).$

These two laws are the distributive laws for conjunction and disjunction. The first of these laws has an analogue in arithmetic and algebra, if we read '$\times$' for '.' and '$+$' for '$\lor$'. It is always true if a, b, and c are real numbers that $(a \times (b + c))$ equals $(a \times b) + (a \times c)$. But there is no similar analogue in arithmetic for RF 13.

RF 14: $(p.q) \equiv \sim (\sim p \lor \sim q).$

RF 15: $(p \lor q) \equiv \sim (\sim p . \sim q).$

RF 14 and 15 are known as *de Morgan's rules* after the English mathematician and logician, Augustus de Morgan. Although he was not the first logician to discover these rules, which were known in the middle ages, he was the first to draw attention to their importance. It will be seen from an examination of the rules, as expressed above, that there is an important relation between conjunction and disjunction. Any expression in which a disjunction occurs may be expressed as a conjunction, if we negate *both components* of the disjunction and also the *disjunction itself*. And similarly, any conjunction may always be expressed as a disjunction, if we negate both components of the conjunction and the conjunction itself. This important relation is known as the *duality* of conjunction and disjunction. It is very useful in logical manipulations.

RF 16: $(p \supset q) \equiv (\sim q \supset \sim p).$—This is the Law of Contraposition. It states that, in any implication, we may interchange antecedent and consequent, provided that we negate them both.

RF 17: $(p \supset q) \equiv (\sim p \lor q).$—This is the definition of material implication which we have met already.

RF 18: $(p \supset q) \equiv \sim(p . \sim q)$.—This can be transformed into RF 17 by applying RF 7 and 14 to the right-hand side of the equivalence. It is another definition of material implication.

RF 19: $((p \supset q) . (q \supset r)) \supset (p \supset r)$.—This is the law of the transitivity of implication. It states that if one expression implies a second and the second implies a third, then the first implies the third.

RF 20: $((p \supset q) . p) \supset q$.—This is known as the *rule of detachment* or the *ponendo ponens* rule. It states that if the antecedent of an implication is affirmed together with the implication, then the consequent of the implication follows.

7. Decision Procedures and Normal Forms.

One of the most important problems in logic is that of finding a method which will enable us to say of any given expression whether or not it is a tautology. The method of truth-tables which was explained above is one such method which is available to us in the calculus of propositions. These methods are called "*decision procedures*", because they enable us to *decide* whether or not an expression is a tautology.

We have seen that the method of truth-tables sometimes becomes unwieldy when there are a large number of propositional variables in the expression whose logical truth is under consideration. There is, however, another decision procedure which is sometimes more convenient to apply than the truth-table method. This is known as the method of reduction to *normal* or *canonical form*.

It was seen above that any of the logical constants of the propositional calculus can be expressed in terms of the other constants. For example, an expression containing the constants '.' and '$\supset$' can be translated into an equivalent expression containing only '$\sim$' and 'v' as constants. Thus:

$$((p \supset q) \cdot (q \supset r)) \supset (p \supset r)$$

is equivalent to:

$$\sim \sim (\sim (\sim p \lor q) \lor \sim (\sim q \lor r)) \lor (\sim p \lor r),$$

by the application of RF 14 and 17 above.

By the use of equivalent expressions in this way, it is possible to transform any expression into an expression consisting of a *conjunction* of disjunctions of the form:

$$((\ldots (p \lor q) \lor \sim q) \lor r) \lor s) \lor \ldots) \lor t.$$

That is to say (1) the disjunction consists only of propositional variables and their negations and these in a standard order (*e.g.* alphabetical), provided that if both a propositional variable and its negation occur, the negated instance immediately succeeds the unnegated instance. (2) The disjunction is bracketed in a standard way, *i.e.* from left to right, a bracket following every propositional variable except the first and last. The conjunction built up from these disjunctions also exhibits a standard ordering and bracketing. It is called a *conjunctive normal form*. We prove first:

THEOREM 1: A conjunction of disjunctions not in standard ordering or bracketing can be converted to an equivalent conjunctive normal form (CNF for short). This can always be accomplished by successive applications of RF 8, 9, 10, 11.

We may convert a formula into an equivalent CNF by proceeding as follows. First we strike out all double negations, according to RF 7. (This process is repeated when necessary after each of the further operations.) Next we replace all occurrences of '$P \supset Q$' by '$\sim P \lor Q$' according to RF 17. Then we get rid of forms like '$\sim (P \lor Q)$', '$\sim (P \cdot Q)$' replacing them with '$\sim P \cdot \sim Q$',

'$\sim P \lor \sim Q$' respectively, according to RF 14, 15, and 7.*

We proceed in this manner until no bracket is preceded by a negation sign. We then transform the resulting formula into a conjunction of disjunctions by repeated applications of RF 12 and 13 and obtain the CNF by RF 8, 9, 10, and 11. This process can always be carried out until a CNF is reached and so we have:

THEOREM 2: Every formula can be reduced to an equivalent CNF by applications of RF 7 to 17.

From this we have immediately:

THEOREM 3: Every tautology can be reduced to a tautological CNF by applications of RF 7 to 17.

That the CNF is equivalent to the original formula is, of course, a consequence of the fact that RF 7 to 17 are themselves tautologies.

We now have to consider the conditions under which a CNF is a tautology. Plainly a conjunction is a tautology if and only if its elements are tautologies. Hence we have:

THEOREM 4: A CNF is a tautology if and only if each of its component disjuncts is a tautology.

Furthermore, we have:

THEOREM 5: A disjunction whose components are propositional variables is a tautology if and only if at least one propositional variable *and its negation* occurs in the disjunction.

If such a disjunction is in standard ordering, the appropriate propositional variable will, of course, immediately precede its negation.

---

* Here we must understand the italic capital letters P, Q, to stand for *any* propositional variable, negated or unnegated, or any truth-functional expression compounded from such variables. (See p. 69.)

The process of reduction to CNF is illustrated in the following examples:

(a) $((p \supset q) . \sim q) \supset \sim p.$

$\sim ((\sim p \vee q) . \sim q) \vee \sim p.$ By RF 17.

$(\sim (\sim p \vee q) \vee \sim \sim q) \vee \sim p.$ By RF 7 and 14.

$((p . \sim q) \vee q) \vee \sim p.$ By RF 7 and 15.

$((q \vee p) . (q \vee \sim q)) \vee \sim p.$ By RF 9 and 13.

$((p \vee \sim p) \vee q) . ((\sim p \vee q) \vee \sim q).$ By RF 9 and 13.

(b) $((p \supset q) . (q \supset r)) \supset (p \supset r).$

First transform the expression by RF 17 into:

$$\sim ((\sim p \vee q) . (\sim q \vee r)) \vee (\sim p \vee r).$$

Applying the de Morgan rule (and dropping double negations by RF 7), we have:

$$(\sim (\sim p \vee q) \vee \sim (\sim q \vee r)) \vee (\sim p \vee r).$$

And a second application of the rule gives:

$$((p . \sim q) \vee (q . \sim r)) \vee (\sim p \vee r).$$

Applying the distributive laws to the first two members of the disjunction, we get:

$$((p \vee q) . (p \vee \sim r) . (q \vee \sim q) . (\sim q \vee \sim r)) \vee (\sim p \vee r).$$

Finally, by the commutative law (RF 9), we can bring the second term of the disjunction to the front of the expression and then apply RF 13 to get:

$(p \vee \sim p \vee q \vee r) . (p \vee \sim p \vee r \vee \sim r).$

$\qquad\qquad (\sim p \vee q \vee \sim q \vee r) . (\sim p \vee \sim q \vee r \vee \sim r).$

The expression is now in conjunctive normal form.

(c) $((p \supset q) . \sim p) \supset \sim q.$

First we apply RF 17 to transform the constants of implication into negation and disjunction signs:

$$\sim ((\sim p \lor q) . \sim p) \lor \sim q.$$

Then we apply the de Morgan rule to transform the conjunction sign in the same way:

$$\sim \sim (\sim (\sim p \lor q) \lor \sim \sim p) \lor \sim q.$$

We next drop the double negation by RF 7 and use the associative law (RF 11) to group the expression as:

$$\sim (\sim p \lor q) \lor (p \lor \sim q)$$

and then apply RF 7 and the de Morgan rule to arrive at:

$$(p . \sim q) \lor (p \lor \sim q).$$

Finally, we switch the order of the elements of the main disjunction by the commutative law and use the distributive law (RF 13) to obtain:

$$(p \lor p \lor \sim q) . (p \lor \sim q \lor \sim q).$$

The expression is now in conjunctive normal form.

If we examine the conjunctive normal forms arrived at in these manipulations, it will be seen that in examples (a) and (b) each member of the conjunction, in both cases, contains *a propositional variable and its negation* joined by '$\lor$'. For instance, the first conjunct of (a) in normal form contains 'p' and '$\sim p$' joined by '$\lor$' and the second conjunct contains 'q' and '$\sim q$' similarly joined. Now this disjunction of a propositional variable and its negation is a tautology. (See RF 2 above.) Moreover, such an expression remains logically true, if we add to it by disjunction any number of propositional variables, whatever their truth-values. In other words, since '$(p \lor \sim p)$' is a tautology, so is '$(p \lor \sim p \lor q)$' and '$(p \lor \sim p \lor q \lor r \lor \ldots)$'. It is obvious, to take a concrete example, that since "either it is raining or it is not raining" is logically true, so is "either it is raining or it is not raining or twice two are five."

Thus each element of the conjunction is logically true and therefore the whole expression in these two cases is logically true. But in the case of (c), this condition does *not* hold. Thus (c) is not logically true.

We can sum the matter up as follows:

(1) '$P \lor \sim P$' is logically true.

(2) If 'P' is logically true, then '$P \lor Q$' is logically true.

(3) If both 'P' and 'Q' are logically true, then '$P . Q$' is logically true.

(Here we must understand the capital letters 'P', 'Q', to stand for any propositional variable, negated or unnegated, or any truth-functional expression compounded from propositional variables.)

8. The Total Number of Truth-Functional Expressions. It has been seen that, when we evaluate a truth-functional expression by constructing its truth-table, we determine its characteristic matrix-number. Thus the matrix-number of '$p \lor q$' is 1110 and that of '$p.(q \lor r)$' is 11100000. We have seen also that any two or more expressions which are *logically equivalent* have the same matrix-number and, in particular, all tautologies have the number 1111 for functions of two variables, 11111111 for functions of three variables, and so on. Suppose now that we ask the question "how many *non-equivalent* truth-functions are there in the propositional calculus?"

Obviously, the answer to this question will depend on the number of propositional variables which we admit into the calculus, but for any stated number of variables, the answer is easy to give. For the number of non-equivalent truth-functional expressions will be the number of different matrix-numbers. Thus, if we are concerned only with *one* propositional variable, there will be *four* possible matrix-numbers: 11, 10, 01, 00. And these are the respective numbers of the expressions:

$$p \vee \sim p; \quad p; \quad \sim p; \quad p . \sim p.$$

For truth-functional expressions of two variables '*p*' and '*q*' we need, as has been seen, a matrix-number consisting of *four* digits. The number of non-equivalent expressions constructed from '*p*' and '*q*' will therefore be the possible way of filling four places with either or both of the digits 1 and 0. Clearly, this will be 2^4 or sixteen ways, since there are two ways of filling the first place, two ways of filling the second place, each of which has to be combined with the two ways of filling the first place, and so on.

Proceeding in the same way, we see that for three variables '*p*', '*q*', and '*r*' there will be 2^8 or 256 possible non-equivalent expressions, and that for four variables there will be 2^{16} or 65,536. To see what the general formula for *n* variables will be, we notice that the *powers* of 2 in 2^2, 2^4, 2^8, 2^{16} used above are themselves the successive powers of 2, viz. 2^1, 2^2, 2^3, and so on. Thus, the number of non-equivalent truth-functional expressions in the pro-positional calculus can be represented as follows:

There are 2^{2^1} or 2^2 or 4 non-equivalent functions of one variable.

There are 2^{2^2} or 2^4 or 16 non-equivalent functions of two variables.

There are 2^{2^3} or 2^8 or 256 non-equivalent functions of three variables.

And, in general, there will be 2^{2^n} non-equivalent functions of *n* variables.

9. Derivation by Substitution. The method of truth-tables and of normal forms are decision procedures which can be applied to a given formula as a touchstone of validity. They tell us, with respect to any formula, *whether or not* it is a tautology. There is, however, another method by which we may show *that* a given conclusion follows from its premisses and so that a given formula of the form:

(1) $(P_1.P_2.P_3....P_n) \supset Q$

is valid. This is the method of *deriving* the conclusion from the premisses by making use of formulae already established as valid. (Some of the most important of these formulae have been listed in Section 6 as "reference formulae". They are sometimes, rather misleadingly, called "logical laws".) The method of derivation by substitution, to be explained below, is not a decision procedure. For it will not enable us to say of any given formula *whether or not* it is valid. But it will enable us to show that a certain formula is derivable from a set of premisses if, in fact, it is so derivable. It therefore provides a useful method of testing the validity of arguments.

In order to make use of this method we have to assume that if one formula can be obtained from another by interchanging with it formulae known to be equivalent, then the original formula is equivalent to that obtained by the interchange. For example:

(2) $p.(q \lor r)$

is known to be equivalent, by RF 12, to:

(3) $(p.q) \lor (p.r)$.

We may therefore write (3) wherever we find (2) and vice versa. This assumption will be justified later; but for the present, we shall assume it without proof. Thus if we have an expression of the form:

(4) $(P \supset Q) \equiv (R \vee S)$

and we know from our reference formulae that, for example, '$Q \equiv T$' and '$R \equiv \sim U$', then we may write (4) as:

(5) $(P \supset T) \equiv (\sim U \vee S)$.

We shall assume further, in virtue of RF 19 and RF 20, that:

(i) If we have conditional expressions of the form '$P \supset Q$' and '$Q \supset R$', then we may assume the further conditional '$P \supset R$'.

(ii) If we have given a conditional '$P \supset Q$' and the antecedent 'P' is also given, then we may assume the consequent 'Q'. These assumptions can also be justified but they are sufficiently obvious to assume here without proof.

Let us now consider the following examples:

(6) If A leaves the country, then it is false that he is both innocent and secure from arrest. If he submits to an audit of his books, then he is innocent. If he is innocent, then he is secure from arrest. He will submit to an audit of his books. *Therefore:* A will not leave the country.

Let us symbolise the propositions involved in this argument thus:

$A = $ A will leave the country.

$I = $ A is innocent.

$S = $ A is secure from arrest.

$B = $ A will submit to an audit of his books.

We may now represent the four premises and the conclusion thus:

(i) $A \supset \sim (I.S)$.

(ii) $B \supset I$.

(iii) $I \supset S$.

(iv) B.

Therefore: $\sim A$.

We may derive the conclusion by substitution as follows:

(v) $(I.S) \supset \sim A$ (from (i), using RF 7 and 16).

(vi) I (from (ii) and (iv) using RF 20).

(vii) S (from (iii) and (vi) using RF 20).

(viii) $\sim A$ (from (vi), (vii), and (v) using RF 20).

(7) If the price of gold shares falls or boring operations fail, then either Jones will go bankrupt or he will commit suicide. If the boring operations fail or Jones goes bankrupt, then there will be a prosecution. There will not be a prosecution. The price of gold shares will fall. *Therefore:* Jones will commit suicide.

As before, we may symbolise our constituent propositions thus:

G = The price of gold shares will fall.

F = Boring operations will fail.

J = Jones will go bankrupt.

S = Jones will commit suicide.

P = There will be a prosecution.

The argument can then be set out thus:

(i) $(G \lor F) \supset (J \lor S)$.

(ii) $(F \lor J) \supset P$.

(iii) $\sim P$.

(iv) G.

Therefore: S.

(v) $\sim P \supset \sim (F \lor J)$ (from (ii) by RF 16).

(vi) $\sim (F \lor J)$ (from (v) and (iii) by RF 20).

(vii)	$\sim F . \sim J$	(from (vi) by RF 14).
(viii)	$\sim (G \vee F) \vee (J \vee S)$	(from (i) by RF 17).
(ix)	$(\sim G . \sim F) \vee (J \vee S)$	(from (viii) by RF 14).
(x)	$(J \vee S \vee \sim G) . (J \vee S \vee \sim F)$	(from (ix) by RF 13).
(xi)	$(J \vee \sim G \vee S)$	(from (x) by RF 4 and RF 9).
(xii)	$\sim (J \vee \sim G) \supset S$	(from (xi) by RF 17).
(xiii)	$(\sim J . G) \supset S$	(from (xii) by RF 14).
(xiv)	S	(from (vii), (iv), and (xiii) by RF 20).

(8) If it is false that A's flight implies A's guilt, then if the evidence was properly recorded, the police were not impartial. *Therefore:* If A has fled and the evidence was properly recorded, then if the police were impartial, A is guilty.

We may represent the argument as follows:

(i) $\sim (F \supset G) \supset (E \supset \sim I)$.

Therefore: $(F . E) \supset (I \supset G)$.

(ii)	$(F \supset G) \vee (E \supset \sim I)$	(from (i) by RF 17).
(iii)	$(\sim F \vee G) \vee (\sim E \vee \sim I)$	(from (ii) by RF 17).
(iv)	$(\sim F \vee \sim E \vee \sim I \vee G)$	(from (iii) by RF 9 and RF 11).
(v)	$\sim (F . E) \vee (\sim I \vee G)$	(from (iv) RF 14).
(vi)	$(F . E) \supset (I \supset G)$	(from (v) by RF 17).

(9) If this substance is put into hydrochloric acid, then if it dissolves, it is either salt A or salt B. If it is salt A, it contains sodium. If it is salt B, it burns with a red flame. It is put into hydrochloric acid and does dissolve.

It does not burn with a red flame. *Therefore*, it contains sodium.

We have:

   (i) $H \supset (D \supset (A \lor B)$.

   (ii) $A \supset S$.

   (iii) $B \supset R$.

   (iv) $H \cdot D$.

   (v) $\sim R$.

Therefore: S.

(vi)	$D \supset (A \lor B)$	(from (i) and (iv) by RF 20).
(vii)	$A \lor B$	(from (iv) and (vi) by RF 20).
(viii)	$\sim R \supset \sim B$	(from (iii) by RF 16).
(ix)	$\sim B$	(from (v) and (viii) by RF 20).
(x)	$B \lor A$	(from (vii) by RF 9).
(xi)	$\sim B \supset A$	(from (x) by RF 17).
(xii)	A	(from (ix) and (xi) by RF 20).
(xiii)	S	(from (ii) and (xii) by RF 20).

Arguments (6) to (9) above are valid and their validity was shown by use of the reference formulae. It is not possible, however, to show conclusively in this way that a given argument is *invalid*. We shall certainly fail, if the argument is invalid, to make substitutions which lead to the required conclusion. Nevertheless, we cannot always be sure, if the argument is complex, that our failure to arrive at our goal is not due merely to our inability to see what substitutions we ought to make. But in simple cases of invalid arguments, it becomes obvious after a few steps that the conclusion cannot be reached. For example:

(10) If A is elected, B will resign. If C is elected, B will not resign. If A is elected, C will not be elected. Therefore: B will resign.

We have:

(i) $A \supset B.$
(ii) $C \supset \sim B.$
(iii) $A \supset \sim C.$

Therefore: $B.$

It becomes obvious, as soon as the argument is formalised, that we shall never be able to prove the conclusion B from the given premisses. Nevertheless, self-evidence is never a wholly reliable guide as a test of logical validity and it is always desirable to check the findings of intuition by some more objective test. If therefore we suspect that an argument which we are testing by this means is invalid, we can always fall back upon a decision procedure to give us an unequivocal answer.

BIBLIOGRAPHICAL NOTE

CHAPTERS II AND III

Good treatments of the truth-table method of decision are given in Ambrose and Lazerowitz (1), Cooley (7), and Reichenbach (25). The classical exposition of the propositional calculus is in Hilbert and Ackermann (12), but the student should be warned that the manner of presentation is very condensed and demands careful study.

CHAPTER IV

THE AXIOMATIC METHOD

1. The Purpose of the Axiomatic Method. The decision procedures which we have discussed so far enable us to distinguish the truth-functional expressions which are tautologies or logical laws from those which are not. But they do not give us any means of *constructing* tautologies. For that we need a procedure of quite a different kind. We have such a procedure in the *axiomatic method* which is familiar to most people, in a rather imperfect form, in the geometry of Euclid. In using this method, we choose a number of propositions known as axioms (or postulates) as our starting point, and with the help of certain definitions deduce other propositions (known as *theorems*) from the axioms. The use of the axiomatic method in logic is similar but we need to be more careful and specific about our starting point than we need be in Euclidean geometry. For Euclidean geometry assumes without mentioning the ordinary procedures of logical inference. And we may not, of course, do this in constructing an axiomatic basis for a part of logic itself.

Before we go on to lay down the basis of the axiomatic system and use it in making deductions, it would be well to recapitulate a little in order to make clear the purpose of the axiomatic method. We have seen that the truth-functional expressions of the propositional calculus are built up from three different kinds of basic material, (i) propositional variables, (ii) logical constants, and (iii) brackets which express the scope of the logical constants. It is, however, not permitted to put this material together in any order we please. Certain combinations of this material make up truth-functional expressions; certain others do not. For example: '$(p \supset q) \equiv (\sim q \supset \sim p)$' and '$(p \vee q) \supset r$' are both permitted expressions. But '$\supset \sim qp$' or '$p \sim \equiv q \supset$' are not. We have so far taken this distinction as intuitively obvious but we now need to make it explicit. We shall do so by distinguishing all the possible combinations of the basic material into two classes, (i) meaningful or permitted expressions, called "*well-formed formulae*"; (ii) meaningless or illegitimate combinations such as '$p \equiv . \vee q \vee$'. There is a corresponding distinction in ordinary language between sentences constructed according to the rules of grammar and syntax and random combinations of words like "is over very cats between" which would ordinarily be said to be meaningless. The precise distinction between meaningful and meaningless sentences in ordinary language is not an easy one to draw, though the extremes of meaninglessness are obvious enough. But in logic it is fortunately possible to make the corresponding distinction quite precise by definite rules.

Of these two types of expression, we are, of course, interested only in well-formed formulae. But these also fall into two main classes, those which are *tautologies* or *logically true* (distinguished in their truth-tables by having only 1's in the main column) and those which are not logically true but are either contradictory or contingent. Again we are interested primarily in the first of these two classes. We use the axiomatic method in order to construct, on the foundation of certain basic material, expressions *all of which* are tautologies. These we can again subdivide into those which we take as the *starting point* of our axiom system and those which we leave to be *proved in the system*. The members of the first set we call *axioms* (or *postulates*) and the members of the second set we call *derivable formulae* or *theorems*.

We can represent the relations between these various types of expressions as follows:

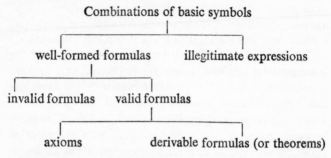

Combinations of basic symbols

well-formed formulas   illegitimate expressions

invalid formulas   valid formulas

axioms   derivable formulas (or theorems)

The basic material which we need in order to build up an axiom system is as follows:

(i) Rules of syntax.

(ii) Definitions.

(iii) Axioms.

Let us consider each of these in turn.

2. The Construction of an Axiom System. *Rules of Syntax.*—The word "syntax" is used in logic as a technical term but its technical meaning is analogous to that which it bears in ordinary language. The original meaning of "syntax", according to the *Oxford English Dictionary*, was "the orderly or systematic arrangement of parts or elements". In time, the use of the word became specialised and its usually accepted meaning is given, by the same dictionary, as "the arrangement of words, in their appropriate forms, by which their connection and relation in a sentence are shown". In logic, the phrase "logical syntax" (or, for short, "syntax") refers to the rules which govern the relations between the symbols of logic. There are two main classes of such rules. Those which govern the construction of *well-formed formulae* (which for short, we shall call WFF's) are known as *formation* rules. But we also need rules which determine when a proposition can be said *to be a consequence of* or *follow from* one or more propositions. These are known as *transformation rules*. Let us now consider these rules in detail:

Formation Rules.—RSF 1: (A rule determining the primitive categories or concepts of the propositional calculus.) There are *three* such categories.

(i) The symbols p, q, r . . . (or, alternatively, p_1, p_2, p_3, . . . p_n) stand for propositional variables, that is, represent indifferently *any* proposition whatever.

(ii) Logical constants consisting of an initial constant '$\sim$' and the binary constants '$.$', 'v', '$\supset$', and '$\equiv$'.

(iii) The concept of the *scope of constants* expressed by brackets '$(. . .)$'.

RSF 2: (This rule governs the formation of WFF's.)

(i) A propositional variable is a WFF.

(ii) If 'P' is a WFF, then '$\sim P$' is a WFF.

(iii) Any two WFF's joined by a binary constant is a WFF.

(Thus, if 'P' and 'Q' are both WFF's, then '$P . Q$', '$P \vee Q$', '$P \supset Q$', and '$P \equiv Q$' are all WFF's.)

RSF 3: (This rule determines how the expressions of the propositional calculus are to be punctuated in order to be unambiguous and thus how the scope of constants is to be understood.)

(i) The relative strength of the binary constants, from strongest to weakest, shall be as follows:

$$. \vee \supset \equiv$$

For example, the expressions:

(A) $p.q \supset r \vee s$,

(B) $p.q \vee r \equiv s$,

(C) $p \supset q.r \vee \sim s$,

shall be read, in the absence of brackets, as if bracketed thus:

(A') $(p.q) \supset (r \vee s)$,

(B') $((p.q) \vee r) \equiv s$,

(C') $p \supset ((q.r) \vee \sim s)$.

(ii) Where brackets are used to indicate the scope of constants (either to avoid ambiguity or to facilitate understanding) the following rules shall apply:

(*a*) If '$\sim$' is immediately followed by a propositional variable the scope of '$\sim$' is confined *to that variable*. If it is followed by a left-hand bracket '(', the scope of '$\sim$' extends to the corresponding right-hand bracket. (For examples, see Chapter III, Section 2, above.)

(*b*) If a binary constant is flanked by a propositional variable, the scope of the constant *on that flank* is confined to the variable. If a binary constant is flanked by a bracket, the scope of the constant extends to the *corresponding* bracket. (For examples see above.)

(*c*) The definition of a *corresponding bracket* to a left-hand bracket is the $(n + 1)$th right-hand bracket *succeeding* if n left-hand brackets intervene. Analogously, the corresponding bracket to a right-hand bracket is the $(n + 1)$th left-hand bracket *preceding* if n right-hand brackets intervene.

For example, consider the expression:

$$(((p \supset q) \supset (p \supset r)) \supset (q \supset r)) \vee (s \vee t).$$

Here the corresponding bracket to the first left-hand bracket is the *fifth* right-hand bracket; the corresponding bracket to the third right-hand bracket is the *second* bracket; and so on.

Metalogical Symbols.—The capital letters '*P*', '*Q*', '*R*', ... shall be used as metalogical symbols. These may be regarded as *second-order variables* whose values are WFF's formed according to RSF 2 above. These symbols are accordingly used to represent propositions whose logical form is left indeterminate. (An example of their use occurs in Chapter III, Section 7, above.) Thus '*P* ∨ *Q*' can stand indifferently for any WFF whose constant of widest scope is a disjunction. Similarly, '∼*P*' can stand for any negated expression whatsoever. Symbols of this type are required in order to express the *transformation rules* of the system in a general form. They are not *used in* the axiomatic system but are required to *talk about* the system. They are therefore said to belong to the *metalanguage* of propositional logic.

Transformation Rules.—*RST 1: Rule of Uniform Substitution.*—Any WFF may be substituted for any propositional variable *throughout an expression.* Thus, for:

$$((p \supset q) . \sim q) \supset \sim p$$

we may write:

$$(((p \lor q) \supset q) . \sim q) \supset \sim (p \lor q),$$

substituting '(*p* ∨ *q*)' for '*p*' throughout. We express the fact that this substitution has been made by writing '(*p* ∨ *q*)/*p*' beside the new formula.*

RST 2: Rule of Substitution by Definition.—In any valid formula (that is, in any axiom or theorem), we may

---

* The stroke here is, of course, not the constant of the stroke function (which has not been introduced into this axiomatic system) but merely represents the operation of substituting in accordance with RST 1.

substitute *for any part* of the formula any expression which is equivalent to it by definitions Def. 1 to Def. 3 below.

Thus, for: $((p \supset q).(q \supset r)) \supset (p \supset r)$

we may write: $\sim ((p \supset q).(q \supset r)) \vee (p \supset r)$,

in accordance with Def. 2. Similarly, we may write the same expression in accordance with this rule but using Def. 1, as: $\sim (\sim (p \supset q) \vee \sim (q \supset r)) \supset (p \supset r)$.

Notice that substitution in accordance with RST 2 need not be made *throughout the formula*, as in the case of RST 1.

RST 3: Rule of Detachment.—If '$P \supset Q$' and 'P' are both valid formulae, then 'Q' is a valid formula.

RST 4: Rule of Adjunction.—If 'P' is a valid formula and 'Q' is a valid formula then '$P.Q$' is a valid formula.

[*Note.*—This rule is stated here for convenience only. It is not strictly necessary to state it separately and it is proved below. (See page 90 and the discussion of independence in Section 6.)]

The syntactical rules given above are sufficient to enable us to set out the axiomatic system but it is possible, and also useful, to prove further rules of syntax as they are required.

Definitions.

Def. 1. $P.Q =_{df} \sim (\sim P \vee \sim Q)$.

Def. 2. $P \supset Q =_{df} \sim P \vee Q$.

Def. 3. $P \equiv Q =_{df} (P \supset Q).(Q \supset P)$.

Axioms.—We may choose the axioms of our system in a very large number of different ways but whatever choice we make there are certain conditions to which our selection must conform. In the first place, our axioms and rules must be consistent. This means that only tautologies should be derivable. A necessary (but not a sufficient) condition for this is that if any formula is derivable, its negation must not be derivable. A more detailed discussion of this point, together with a proof of the consistency of our axioms, will be given later.

There is a second property which it is necessary that a set of axioms should possess if it is to form a satisfactory basis for a system of logic. It must provide an adequate basis for proving *all* the tautologies of the logic in question. In technical terms, the set of axioms must be *complete*. And a third property of our axiom set which, though not strictly necessary, is nevertheless very desirable is that the axioms should be *independent*; in other words, no one of the axioms can be proved as a theorem from the others and, therefore, no one of the axioms is redundant.

We shall later have to discuss these requirements in more detail and to prove that the axioms which we select do, in fact, possess these properties under the rules given. The following axioms are four of the five which were used by Whitehead and Russell in the system of propositional logic set out in *Principia Mathematica*. (The fifth of their axioms was subsequently proved not to be independent of the other four.)

A 1. $(p \lor p) \supset p$.

A 2. $q \supset (p \lor q)$.

A 3. $(p \lor q) \supset (q \lor p)$.

A 4. $(q \supset r) \supset ((p \lor q) \supset (p \lor r))$.

When we meet these axioms for the first time, their most noticeable feature is their triviality. This feature is brought out very clearly if we *interpret* them by replacing the propositional variables by particular propositions. For example, the first axiom, so interpreted might read:

"If it is raining or it is raining, then it is raining".

And A 2 might be interpreted as:

"If it is snowing, then either it is raining or it is snowing".

The reader may well be tempted to wonder how such empty and pointless statements could possibly be of any value as the foundation of a system of logic. The answer is that though the *content* of these axioms is trivial and empty, their *consequences*, that is to say the theorems which can be deduced from them in accordance with the rules of syntax, are by no means always so trivial. After all, if the system of axioms is *complete*, then it will be a basis for proving *all* the tautologies of the system whether obvious or surprising. We shall prove later that this system is complete.

3. Derivable Formulae. For the sake of brevity, we shall refer to the set of axioms, rules, and definitions of the previous section as the Axiom System, or for short, AX. We must first explain precisely what is meant by saying that a particular formula is a *derivable formula of AX* or *provable in AX*.

Suppose we have a formula F, and suppose we are able to form a chain of formulae $P_1, P_2, \ldots P_n, F$ which satisfies the following condition:

Every formula in $P_1, P_2, \ldots P_n, F$ is either an axiom of AX or else it is got from some previous members of the chain by a single application of one of the rules RST 1-3. Such a chain of formulae, if it exists, is called a *derivation* or *proof* of 'F' in AX. The reader will easily see that our condition is simply a precise and explicit statement of what we intuitively understand to be a proof in AX. A formula 'F' then is said to be derivable or provable in AX if there exists a proof of it. Needless to say, there may be many different proofs of the same formula.

EXAMPLE 1.—'$(p \supset \sim p) \supset \sim p$' is a derivable formula of *AX*.

Proof.—We form a chain of formulae, starting with Axiom 1.

$$(1) \quad (p \lor p) \supset p.$$

We now substitute '$\sim p$' for 'p' in (1) according to RST 1,

$$(2) \quad (\sim p \lor \sim p) \supset \sim p.$$

We then put '$p \supset \sim p$' for '$\sim p \lor \sim p$' in (2) according to Def. 2 and RST 2,

$$(3) \quad (p \supset \sim p) \supset \sim p.$$

The chain of formulae (1) to (3) then forms a proof of (3) in *AX*.

We can set out the working formally as follows:

(1) $(p \lor p) \supset p$ A 1.

(2) $(\sim p \lor \sim p) \supset \sim p$ (1), RST 1, $(\sim p/p)$.

(3) $(p \supset \sim p) \supset \sim p$ (2), RST 2, Def. 2.

EXAMPLE 2.—'$(q \supset r) \supset ((p \supset q) \supset (p \supset r))$' is a derivable formula.

Proof.—

(1) $(q \supset r) \supset ((p \lor q) \supset (p \lor r))$ A 4.

(2) $(q \supset r) \supset ((\sim p \lor q) \supset (\sim p \lor r))$ (1), RST 1, $\sim p/p$.

(3) $(q \supset r) \supset ((p \supset q) \supset (p \supset r))$ (2), RST 2, Def. 2.

EXAMPLE 3.—'$\sim p \lor p$' is derivable.

Proof.—

(1) $(q \supset r) \supset ((p \supset q) \supset (p \supset r))$ Example 2.

(2) $((p \lor p) \supset p) \supset ((p \supset (p \lor p)) \supset (p \supset p))$ (1), RST 1, $(p \lor p)/q$, p/r.

(3) $(p \lor p) \supset p$ A 1.

(4) $((p \supset (p \lor p)) \supset (p \supset p))$ (2), (3), RST 3.

(5) $p \supset (p \lor p)$ A 2, RST 1, p/q.

(6) $p \supset p$ (4), (5), RST 3.

(7) $\sim p \lor p$ (6), RST 2, Def. 2.

In what follows, we need to consider, in addition to derivable formulae of AX, *theorems about AX*. Theorems about AX are not themselves derivable formulae; they are rather true statements to the effect that certain formulae are derivable (or are not derivable) and the like. It is clear that derivation in AX may establish the derivability of a formula in AX, but no amount of such derivation will establish that any formula is *not* derivable, or that an infinite number of formulae of a certain kind are derivable. In order to establish theorems of this kind we have to transcend AX, as it were, and view it as the object of investigation.

For this reason we shall not undertake the derivation of random formulae, since this is a matter of little interest by itself. Instead, our efforts will be directed to proving certain facts about AX, namely, its consistency, the independence of its axioms and the completeness of the system. The first two objects may be attained without deriving any new formulae. We shall therefore deal with these first. The question of completeness is more complicated and to answer it, we shall need to investigate the structure of AX in some detail.

4. Conditions for an Axiom System. It has already been stated that we may select the axioms which form the starting point of our system in very many different ways. Nevertheless, our selection may not be quite arbitrary. There are certain considerations, partly of convenience and partly of necessity, which restrict our range of choice. For example, it is inelegant and sometimes awkward to use a needlessly large set of axioms. And our proofs may become unnecessarily complicated and difficult if we restrict ourselves to too small a number. Moreover, it is usually desirable to choose those axioms which will render the proofs of important theorems simple and straight-forward.

But apart from these optional requirements of elegance and simplicity, there are more important demands which any set of axioms must satisfy. These are the conditions of *consistency* and *completeness* which must now be defined with more precision. All our definitions will take as given the formation and transformation rules, so that when we speak of the consistency or completeness of an axiom set, we shall mean consistency or completeness under these rules. In general, an axiom set may be consistent or complete under one set of transformation rules and incon-sistent or incomplete under another set of such rules. For example, although our axioms are both consistent and complete under rules RST 1-4, if we added another rule, say,

RST 5.—If any formula '*P*' is derivable, so is '$\sim P$'

then the axioms would be *inconsistent* under this extended set of rules. Likewise, if we delete, say RST 3, the axioms would be *incomplete* under RST 1, 2, and 4 alone. Deletion of RST 4, on the other hand, would not affect either con-sistency or completeness and it is included only for the sake of convenience.

Three distinct definitions of consistency may be given for an axiom set, assuming RST 1-4. These are:

(1) An axiom set is consistent if every derivable formula is a tautology.

(2) An axiom set is consistent if, for every formula '*P*', '*P*', and '$\sim P$' are not both derivable.

(3) An axiom set is consistent if there are formulae which are not derivable.

It is easy to see that any axiom set which is consistent in sense (1) must also be consistent in senses (2) and (3). This follows from the facts that not every formula is a tautology and that if 'P' is a tautology, '$\sim P$' is not a tautology, and conversely. It is therefore independent of our choice of transformation rules. We shall in fact prove that our axiom set is consistent in sense (1), given the rules RST 1-4.

An axiom set is said to be *complete* if the addition of any further formula (not already derivable) to the axioms results in inconsistency. That is to say, the set is complete if it cannot be extended without running into inconsistency. Since completeness is defined in this manner in terms of inconsistency, it is plain that there will be three distinct notions of completeness corresponding to the three notions of consistency set out above. Thus:

(1) An axiom set is complete if every extension of it results in the derivability of some formulae which are not tautologies.

(2) An axiom set is complete if every extension of it results in the derivability of both 'P' and '$\sim P$', for some formula 'P'.

(3) An axiom set is complete if every extension of it results in the derivability of all formulae.

It is again easy to see that any axiom set which is complete in sense (3) is also complete in senses (1) and (2).

Our next task is to investigate the relations between the three kinds of consistency and completeness for our axiom system AX. We shall ultimately prove that, so far as AX is concerned, the three notions of consistency are equivalent. That is to say, if AX is consistent in any one of the senses of "consistent", it must also be consistent in the other two senses. Likewise, if AX is complete, in any one of the senses of "complete", then it must also be complete in the other two senses. We prove these equivalences for AX only. There are, of course, other systems for which they do not hold.

We have already:

THEOREM 1: If AX is consistent in sense (1), it is also consistent in senses (2) and (3).

THEOREM 2: If AX is complete in sense (3), it is also complete in senses (1) and (2).

It is also obvious that:

THEOREM 3: If AX is consistent in sense (2), it is also consistent in sense (3).

We now prove:

THEOREM 4: If AX is consistent in sense (3), it is also consistent in sense (2).

In other words, if there are formulae not derivable in AX, then for any formula 'P', not both 'P' and '$\sim P$' are derivable in AX. We proceed by proving that if for any formula 'P', both 'P' and '$\sim P$' are derivable, then every formula is derivable. A formal derivation is as follows:

(1) P (given as derivable).

(2) $\sim P$ „   „   „

(3) $\sim P \supset (p \vee \sim P)$ A2, RST 1, $\sim P/q$.

(4) $(p \vee \sim P)$ (2), (3), RST 3.

(5) $(p \vee \sim P) \supset (\sim P \vee p)$ A3, RST 1, $\sim P/q$.

(6) $\sim P \vee p$ (4), (5), RST 3.

(7) $P \supset p$ (6), RST 2, Def 2.

(8) p (1), (7), RST 3.

(9) Q (8), RST 1, Q/p.

where 'Q' is *any* formula.

Thus if both 'P' and '$\sim P$' are derivable, so is any arbitrarily chosen formula 'Q'. Notice that this proof of Theorem 4 depends on the following features of AX: A2, A3, RST 1, RST 2, RST 3. Evidently the theorem will hold for any system incorporating these features.

In order to establish our equivalences, it remains only to prove the following:

THEOREM 5: If AX is consistent in sense (2), it is also consistent in sense (1).

This theorem, however, is more difficult and we shall defer its proof until we have actually established the consistency and completeness of AX.

5. Consistency. How are we to know whether or not a given set of axioms is consistent or not? Clearly it would be impractical to deduce theorems from the axioms until we arrive at a theorem which contradicts a formula already established as valid. For however long we persist with our deductions, we can never be certain whether the contradiction still remains to be discovered or whether the axioms are, after all, consistent. Fortunately, there is a more practical method of deciding whether or not our axioms are consistent. We do so by a procedure equivalent to the truth-table method by which we decide whether or not a given WFF of the propositional calculus is a tautology. We construct what is called a "finite model" in the following way. Let the propositional variables 'p', 'q', 'r'... be regarded as before as taking one or other of two numerical values. We need not, however, *interpret* these values as we did previously when we regarded '1' as representing "true" and '0' as representing "false". Let us merely say that each variable may take one (and only one) of the two values 1 and 2 on any particular occasion of its occurrence.

Let us further define ~ 1 as 2 and ~ 2 as 1, thus:

(a)

	$\sim$
1	2
2	1

Again, we define the values of compound propositions linked by the constant 'V' by considering the constant as an operator analogous to the multiplication sign in arithmetic, so that we can construct a "multiplication table" for it, as follows:

(b)
$$1 \vee 1 = 1$$
$$1 \vee 2 = 2$$
$$2 \vee 1 = 2$$
$$2 \vee 2 = 2$$

or, more concisely and conveniently,

V	1	2
1	1	2
2	2	2

By using tables (a) and (b) we can evaluate any WFF and assign to it one of the two values 1 or 2 for each combination of values of the propositional variables. For example:

p	q	$\sim p \vee q$
1	1	$2 \vee 1 = 2$
1	2	$2 \vee 2 = 2$
2	1	$1 \vee 1 = 1$
2	2	$1 \vee 2 = 2$

Thus '$\sim p \vee q$' takes the value 2 for three of the four possible cases and the value 1 for the remaining case where $p = 2$ and $q = 1$.

Now let us evaluate, by this means, the axioms which we selected above. We shall, first of all, have to write them in terms of '$\sim$' and 'V' thus:

A 1. '$(p \vee p) \supset p$' becomes '$\sim (p \vee p) \vee p$'.

A 2. '$q \supset (p \lor q)$' becomes '$\sim q \lor (p \lor q)$'.

A 3. '$(p \lor q) \supset (q \lor p)$' becomes '$\sim (p \lor q) \lor (q \lor p)$'.

A 4. '$(q \supset r) \supset ((p \lor q) \supset (p \lor r))$' becomes
'$\sim (\sim q \lor r) \lor (\sim (p \lor q) \lor (p \lor r))$'.

Now evaluate them in accordance with (a) and (b) above as follows:

A 1.

$\sim$	$(p$	$\lor$	$p)$	$\lor$	p
2	1	1	1	2	1
1	2	2	2	2	2

A 2.

$\sim$	q	$\lor$	$(p$	$\lor$	$q)$
2	1	2	1	1	1
1	2	2	1	2	2
2	1	2	2	2	1
1	2	2	2	2	2

A 3.

$\sim$	$(p$	$\lor$	$q)$	$\lor$	$(q$	$\lor$	$p)$
2	1	1	1	2	1	1	1
1	1	2	2	2	2	2	1
1	2	2	1	2	1	2	2
1	2	2	2	2	2	2	2

A 4.

$\sim$	$(\sim q$	$\lor$	$r)$	$\lor$	$(\sim$	$(p$	$\lor$	$q)$	$\lor$	$(p$	$\lor$	$r))$
1	2 1	2	1	2	2	1	1	1	2	1	1	1
1	2 1	2	2	2	2	1	1	1	2	1	2	2
2	1 2	1	1	2	1	1	2	2	1	1	1	1
1	1 2	2	2	2	1	1	2	2	2	1	2	2
1	2 1	2	1	2	1	2	2	1	2	2	2	1
1	2 1	2	2	2	1	2	2	1	2	2	2	2
2	1 2	1	1	2	1	2	2	2	2	2	2	1
1	1 2	2	2	2	1	2	2	2	2	2	2	2

It will be seen that each of the axioms takes only the value 2. Now if we can show that this property is retained when the axioms are subjected to the transformation rules of the system, it will follow that all theorems which can be deduced from the axioms likewise take only the value 2. And, if this is so, no two contradictory theorems will be provable in the system. For of any two contradictory theorems, if one takes the value 2, the other must take the value 1, since $\sim 2 = 1$. We have therefore to show that the property which the axioms possess of taking only the value 2 is unaltered by the application of the transformation rules of the system.

It is easy to show that the rules of substitution (RST 1 and 2) cannot affect this property. In the case of RST 2 (the rule of substitution by definition) the conclusion is obvious. For since '$P \supset Q$', for instance, is *defined* as equivalent to '$\sim P \lor Q$', the substitution of '$P \supset Q$' for '$\sim P \lor Q$' cannot possibly affect any of the values taken by a given expression. And the case is similar for the other defined equivalences. And it is hardly less obvious that any expression which is the result of applying RST 1 to any of the axioms cannot take a value other than 2. For the method by which we have evaluated the axioms and ascertained that they take the constant value 2 ensures that we have taken account of *all the possible combinations* of the values of the individual propositional variables. A uniform substitution of a WFF for a given propositional variable throughout an axiom in accordance with RST 1 could result in the axiom taking the value 1 on only one condition. That condition is that such a substitution could add to the number of combinations of 1's and 2's involved in the evaluation of the expression. And this is impossible since the method we have used takes account of *all the possible combinations*.

We can also see that application of the rule of inference (RST 3) to any two valid formulas cannot result in the establishment of a formula which takes the value 1 for any combination of its constituent propositional variables. For any formulas which are validly deduced from the axioms by the application of RST 1 and 2 will, as we have seen, take only the value 2. And if we deduce 'Q' as a consequence from two established formulas 'P' and '$P \supset Q$', we may argue as follows to show that 'Q' must take only the value 2. Both 'P' and '$P \supset Q$', being established as valid, will take only the value 2. Now since $P = 2$, $\sim P = 1$. Therefore, since '$P \supset Q$' is equivalent to '$\sim P \vee Q$', and since '$\sim P \vee Q$' takes the value 2 and '$\sim P$' takes the value 1, 'Q' must take the value 2. [If it did not, then $(1 \vee 1) = 2$, contrary to our definitions.]

Lastly, we can show that the rule of adjunction (RST 4) when applied to any two valid formulas cannot result in the conjunction of the two formulas taking the value 1. We have to show, in other words, that if 'P' and 'Q' each take the value 2, then '$P . Q$' must likewise take the value 2. We know that '$P . Q$' is equivalent to '$\sim (\sim P \vee \sim Q)$'. Thus 2.2 is equivalent to $\sim (\sim 2 \vee \sim 2)$ which is equivalent to $\sim (1 \vee 1)$ or ~ 1, *i.e.* 2. Thus no application of the transformation rules of the system to the four axioms, or to any deducible consequences of the axioms, can result in an expression taking only the value ~ 2 or 1. Thus the axiom set is consistent.

6. Independence. A set of axioms is independent if no member of the set can be proved as a theorem on the basis of some or all of the other members of the set. It is not a radical defect of logic in an axiomatic system if the axioms should prove not to be independent. Nevertheless, it is a defect of elegance and economy if an expression which is, in fact, deducible as a theorem is used as an unproved starting point. For this reason, logicians always try to ensure that the axioms which they select as their starting point are independent in this sense.

But how are we to ascertain whether or not our axioms are in fact independent? Clearly, it is not practical to prove the independence of A 4, for instance, from A 1-3 by trying to prove A 4 from A 1-3 and taking our failure as evidence of independence. For, as we have already remarked in discussing consistency, we could never be certain, however long we persisted with such a method, that A 4 could *not* be so proved. But again the method of constructing finite models offers us a direct means of finding out whether or not the axioms which we select as the starting point of our system are independent of one another. We proceed as before by assigning numerical values to the propositional variables comprising the axioms in such a way that all the possible combinations of numbers assignable to the variables are exhausted. And we construct tables showing the effect of the operators '$\sim$' and '$\vee$' on the values assigned.

Let us first of all prove the independence of A 1 from A 2, A 3, and A 4. We postulate that the propositional variables may take any one of the three values 0, 1, and 2. The operators '$\sim$' and '$\vee$' shall be understood as follows:

(a)

	$\sim$
0	1
1	0
2	2

(b)

$\vee$	0	1	2
0	0	0	0
1	0	1	2
2	0	2	0

Thus, for example, $\sim 1 = 0$ and $\sim 2 = 2$; and $2 \vee 0 = 0$, $2 \vee 1 = 2$, and so on. We can now evaluate axioms A 1-4 as follows, after first stating them, as for the proof of consistency, in terms of the constants '$\sim$' and '$\vee$'.

A 1.

~	(p	V	p)	V	p
1	0	0	0	0	0
0	1	1	1	0	1
1	2	0	2	2	2

A 2.

~	q	V	(p	V	q)
1	0	0	0	0	0
0	1	0	0	0	1
2	2	0	0	0	2
1	0	0	1	0	0
0	1	0	1	1	1
2	2	0	1	2	2
1	0	0	2	0	0
0	1	0	2	2	1
2	2	0	2	0	2

A 3.

~	(p	V	q)	V	(q	V	p)
1	0	0	0	0	0	0	0
1	0	0	1	0	1	0	0
1	0	0	2	0	2	0	0
1	1	0	0	0	0	0	1
0	1	1	1	0	1	1	1
2	1	2	2	0	2	2	1
1	2	0	0	0	0	0	2
2	2	2	1	0	1	2	2
1	2	0	2	0	2	0	2

A 4.

~	(~	q	V	r)	V	(~	(p	V	q)	V	(p	V	r))
1	1	0	0	0	0	1	0	0	0	0	0	0	0
0	1	0	1	1	0	1	0	0	0	0	0	0	1
2	1	0	2	2	0	1	0	0	0	0	0	0	2
1	0	1	0	0	0	1	0	0	1	0	0	0	0
1	0	1	0	1	0	1	0	0	1	0	0	0	1
1	0	1	0	2	0	1	0	0	1	0	0	0	2
1	2	2	0	0	0	1	0	0	2	0	0	0	0
2	2	2	2	1	0	1	0	0	2	0	0	0	1
1	2	2	0	2	0	1	0	0	2	0	0	0	2
1	1	0	0	0	0	1	1	0	0	0	1	0	0
0	1	0	1	1	0	1	1	0	0	1	1	1	1
2	1	0	2	2	0	1	1	0	0	2	1	2	2
1	0	1	0	0	0	0	1	1	1	0	1	0	0
1	0	1	0	1	0	0	1	1	1	0	1	1	1
1	0	1	0	2	0	0	1	1	1	0	1	2	2
1	2	2	0	0	0	2	1	2	2	0	1	0	0
2	2	2	2	1	0	2	1	2	2	2	1	1	1
1	2	2	0	2	0	2	1	2	2	0	1	2	2
1	1	0	0	0	0	1	2	0	0	0	2	0	0
0	1	0	1	1	0	1	2	0	0	2	2	2	1
2	1	0	2	2	0	1	2	0	0	0	2	0	2
1	0	1	0	0	0	2	2	2	1	0	2	0	0
1	0	1	0	1	0	2	2	2	1	0	2	2	1
1	0	1	0	2	0	2	2	2	1	0	2	0	2
1	2	2	0	0	0	1	2	0	2	0	2	0	0
2	2	2	2	1	0	1	2	0	2	2	2	2	1
1	2	2	0	2	0	1	2	0	2	0	2	0	2

It will be seen from a comparison of these tables that A 2, A 3, and A 4 take only the value 0, whereas A 1 takes also the value 2 (for the case where $p = 2$). And it has already been shown in the proof of consistency that the application of the transformation rules to the axioms cannot result in the valid formulas so deduced taking any new values. Thus no deductions from A 2-4 can give any expression which takes any value other than 0. And, in particular, A 1 cannot be so deduced. Thus the independence of A 1 from A 2-4 is proved.

Similar methods will establish the independence of the other axioms but it will not be necessary to set out the details of the evaluations. (The reader should work them out himself for practice.) We may demonstrate the independence of A 2 by evaluating the axioms in accordance with the following tables:

(c)

	$\sim$
0	2
1	1
2	0

(d)

V	0	1	2
0	0	0	0
1	0	1	2
2	0	2	2

Evaluation of the axioms in accordance with these tables gives the following results. A 1, A 3, and A 4 take only the values 0 and 1; but A 2 takes in addition the value 2 (for $p = 2$ and $q = 1$). Thus A 2 is independent of the other three axioms.

The independence of A 3 may be shown by evaluating the axioms in accordance with the following tables:

(e)

	$\sim$
0	1
1	0
2	0
3	2

(f)

V	0	1	2	3
0	0	0	0	0
1	0	1	2	3
2	0	2	2	0
3	0	3	3	3

This model gives only the value 0 for A 1, A 2, and A 4, but A 3 takes also the value 3 for the case where $p = 2$ and $q = 3$. For here we have: $(\sim (2 \text{ V } 3) \text{ V } (3 \text{ V } 2))$ $= (\sim 0 \text{ V } 3) = (1 \text{ V } 3) = 3$. [It should be noted that as in this model the propositional variables can take any one of the *four* values 0, 1, 2, and 3, the evaluation tables are proportionally more complex. We need four rows for A 1; sixteen (or 4^2) rows for A 2 and A 3; and sixty-four (or 4^3)

for A 4, which contains the *three* propositional variables p, q, and r.]

Lastly, the independence of A 4 can be shown by a model constructed as follows:

(g)	$\sim$
0	1
1	0
2	3
3	0

(h) $\vee$	0	1	2	3
0	0	0	0	0
1	0	1	2	3
2	0	2	2	0
3	0	3	0	3

In this model, A 1-3 can take only the value 0, whereas A 4 takes the value 2, if $p = 2$, $q = 3$, and $r = 1$. Then we have:

$$\sim (\sim 3 \vee 1) \vee (\sim (2 \vee 3) \vee (2 \vee 1))$$

$$= \sim 0 \vee (\sim 0 \vee 2) = 1 \vee (1 \vee 2) = 1 \vee 2 = 2.$$

It is important to notice that the rules of inference, as well as the axioms, must be satisfied by the models we choose. For example, in RST 3, the models must secure that if 'P' and '$P \supset Q$' both take the designated value, in this case the value 0, in the appropriate model, then 'Q' takes the same value. Likewise, if 'P' and 'Q' each take the value 0, then '$P . Q$' must also take the value 0.

7. The Derivation of Formulae. We now give some further derivations. We shall use the sign '$\vdash$' as an abbreviation for "is derivable". Thus '$\vdash p \supset p$' means "'$p \supset p$' is derivable" and so on. We shall also need to say that a certain formula is derivable provided that a certain other formula is derivable. So, for example, we write:

$$p \supset p \vdash p \supset (p \supset p)$$

meaning "'$p \supset (p \supset p)$' is derivable if '$p \supset p$' is derivable" and so on.

The axioms, rules of transformation and definitions of *AX* are reprinted here for convenient reference:

Axioms.—A 1. $(p \lor p) \supset p$. A 2. $q \supset (p \lor q)$.

A 3. $(p \lor q) \supset (q \lor p)$. A 4. $(q \supset r) \supset ((p \lor q) \supset (p \lor r))$.

Rules of Transformation.—RST 1. Uniform Substitution; RST 2. Substitution by Definition; RST 3. Detachment; RST 4. Adjunction.

Definitions.—Def. 1. $P.Q =_{df} \sim (\sim P \lor \sim Q)$.

Def. 2. $P \supset Q =_{df} \sim P \lor Q$.

Def. 3. $P \equiv Q =_{df} (P \supset Q).(Q \supset P)$.

D 1. $(p \supset \sim p) \supset \sim p$.

D 2. $(q \supset r) \supset ((p \supset q) \supset (p \supset r))$.

D 3. $\sim p \lor p$.

These have already been proved (Examples 1-3, Section 3). Given $\vdash P \supset Q$ and $\vdash Q \supset R$, we see from D 2 that $\vdash P \supset R$, no matter what '*P*', '*Q*', and '*R*' may be. Thus we have also the following derived rule:

DR 1. If $\vdash P \supset Q$ and $\vdash Q \supset R$, then $\vdash P \supset R$.

An example of the use of DR 1 is the proof of:

D 4. $p \supset (p \lor q)$.

Proof.—

(1) $p \supset (q \lor p)$	A 2, RST 1, $p/q, q/p$.
(2) $(q \lor p) \supset (p \lor q)$	A 3, RST 1, $q/p, p/q$.
(3) $p \supset (p \lor q)$	(1), (2), DR 1.

It will be seen that an application of DR 1 can always be eliminated in favour of D 2, RST 1, and two applications of RST 3.

D 5. $((p \lor q) \lor r) \supset ((p \lor q) \lor (q \lor r))$.

Proof.—

(1) $r \supset (q \lor r)$	A 2, RST, 1, $r/q, q/p$.

(2) $(r \supset (q \lor r)) \supset (((p \lor q) \lor r)$ $\qquad$ A 4, RST 1, r/q, $(p \lor q)/p$,
$\qquad \supset ((p \lor q) \lor (q \lor r)))$ $\qquad$ $(q \lor r)/r$.

(3) $((p \lor q) \lor r) \supset ((p \lor q)$
$\qquad \lor (q \lor r))$ $\qquad\qquad$ (1), (2), RST 3.

D 6. $(p \lor q) \supset ((r \lor q) \lor p)$.

Proof.—

(1) $q \supset (r \lor q)$ $\qquad\qquad\qquad$ A 2, r/p.

(2) $(q \supset (r \lor q)) \supset ((p \lor q)$
$\qquad \supset (p \lor (r \lor q)))$ $\qquad\qquad$ A 4, RST 1, $(r \lor q)/r$.

(3) $(p \lor q) \supset ((p \lor (r \lor q))$ $\qquad$ (1), (2), RST 3.

(4) $(p \lor (r \lor q)) \supset ((r \lor q) \lor p)$ $\quad$ A 3, $(r \lor q)/q$.

(5) $(p \lor q) \supset ((r \lor q) \lor p)$ $\qquad$ (3), (4), DR 1.

D 7. $(r \lor (p \lor q)) \supset (r \lor (p \lor (q \lor s)))$.

(1) $q \supset (q \lor p)$ $\qquad\qquad\qquad$ A 2, A 3, DR 1.

(2) $q \supset (q \lor s)$ $\qquad\qquad\qquad$ (1), RST 1, s/p.

(3) $(q \supset (q \lor s)) \supset ((p \lor q)$
$\qquad \supset (p \lor (q \lor s)))$ $\qquad\qquad$ A 4, RST 1, $(q \lor s)/r$.

(4) $(p \lor q) \supset (p \lor (q \lor s))$ $\qquad$ (2), (3), RST 3.

(5) $((p \lor q) \supset (p \lor (q \lor s)))$ $\qquad$ A 4, RST 1, r/p,
$\qquad \supset ((r \lor (p \lor q))$ $\qquad\qquad$ $(p \lor q)/q$,
$\qquad \supset (r \lor (p \lor (q \lor s))))$ $\qquad$ $(p \lor (q \lor s))/r$.

(6) $(r \lor (p \lor q))$ $\qquad\qquad\qquad$ (4), (5), RST 3.
$\qquad \supset (r \lor (p \lor (q \lor s)))$

D 8. $((p \lor q) \lor (q \lor r)) \supset (p \lor (q \lor r))$.

Proof.—

(1) $((p \lor q) \lor (q \lor r))$ $\qquad\qquad$ D6, RST 1,
$\qquad \supset ((p \lor (q \lor r)) \lor (p \lor q))$ $\quad$ $(p \lor q)/p$,
$\qquad\qquad\qquad\qquad\qquad\qquad$ $(q \lor r)/p, p/r$.

(2) $((p \lor (q \lor r)) \lor (p \lor q)$ $\qquad$ D 7, RST 1,
$\qquad \supset ((p \lor (q \lor r))$ $\qquad\qquad$ $(p \lor (q \lor r))/r, r/s$.
$\qquad \lor (p \lor (q \lor r)))$

(3) $((p \lor (q \lor r)) \lor (p \lor (q \lor r)))$ A1, RST 1,
     $\supset (p \lor (q \lor r))$ $(p \lor (q \lor r))/p$.

(4) $((p \lor q) \lor (q \lor r))$ (1), (2), DR 1.
     $\supset (p \lor (q \lor r)) \lor (p \lor (q \lor r)))$

(5) $((p \lor q) \lor (q \lor r)) \supset (p \lor (q \lor r))$ (3), (4), DR 1.

D 9. $((p \lor q) \lor r) \supset (p \lor (q \lor r))$.

Proof.—By D 5, D 8, DR 1.

D 10. $(p \lor (q \lor r)) \supset ((p \lor q) \lor r)$.

Proof.—This can be obtained from D 9, using A 3, DR 1, etc., and relettering.

D 11. $p \lor \sim p$.

Proof.—Use A 3, D 3, RST 3.

D 12. $p \supset (q \supset (p . q))$.

Proof.—

(1) $(\sim p \lor \sim q) \lor \sim (\sim p \lor \sim q)$ D 11, RST 1,
     $(\sim p \lor \sim q)/p$.

(2) $(\sim p \lor \sim q) \lor (p . q)$ (1), RST 2, Def. 1.

(3) $((\sim p \lor \sim q) \lor (p . q))$ D 9, $\sim p/p$,
     $\supset (\sim p \lor (\sim q \lor (p . q)))$ $\sim q/q$, $(p . q)/r$

(4) $\sim p \lor (\sim q \lor (p . q))$ (2), (3), RST 3.

(5) $p \supset (q \supset (p . q))$ (4), RST 2, Def. 2.

D 12 gives us a further derived rule:

DR 2. If $\vdash P$ and $\vdash Q$, then $\vdash P . Q$ (Rule of Adjunction, RST 4), (thus proving this rule derivable).

Using D 9, D 10, DR 2, and Def. 3, we obtain:

D 13. $((p \lor q) \lor r) \equiv (p \lor (q \lor r))$.

The following are relatively easy to prove:

D 14. $(p \lor q) \equiv (q \lor p)$.

D 15. $p \supset \sim \sim p$.

D 16. $\sim \sim p \supset p$.

D 17. $\sim\sim p \equiv p.$

D 18. $(p \supset q) \supset (\sim q \supset \sim p).$

D 19. $(\sim q \supset \sim p) \supset (p \supset q).$

D 20. $(\sim q \supset \sim p) \equiv (p \supset q).$

D 21. $(p.q) \supset (q.p).$

D 22. $(p.q) \equiv (q.p).$

D 23. $p \equiv p.$

D 24. $p.q \equiv \sim(\sim p \vee \sim q).$

D 25. $(p \supset q) \equiv (\sim p \vee q).$

D 26. $(p \vee q) \equiv \sim(\sim p.\sim q).$

D 27. $p.(q.r) \equiv (p.q).r.$

D 28. $(p.q) \supset p.$

It will be seen that D 1-28 above include many of the reference formulae set out in Section 6 of the previous chapter. (In particular, RF 7-11 and 14-17.) We still need to derive RF 12 and 13 which are a little more difficult. We first need:

D 29. $(p \supset (p \supset q)) \supset (p \supset q).$

D 30. $(p \supset (q \supset r)) \supset (q \supset (p \supset r)).$

Then we proceed:

D 31. $(p \vee (q.r)) \supset ((p \vee q).(p \vee r)).$

Proof.—

(1) $(q.r) \supset q$ D 28, RST 1, $q/p, r/q.$

(2) $((q.r) \supset q) \supset ((p \vee (q.r)) \supset (p \vee q))$ A 4, RST 1, $(q.r)/q, q/r.$

(3) $(p \vee (q.r)) \supset (p \vee q)$ (1), (2), RST 3.

(4) $(q.p) \supset (p.q)$ D 21, RST 1, $q/p, p/q.$

(5) $(q.r) \supset r$ (4), D 28, DR 1, RST 1, $r/p.$

(6) $(p \vee (q.r)) \supset (p \vee r)$ A 4, RST 1, $(q.r)/q$, (5), RST 3.

(7) $(p \lor q) \supset ((p \lor r)$ D 12, RST 1, $(p \lor q)/p$.
        $\supset ((p \lor q).(p \lor r)))$ $(p \lor r)/q$.

(8) $(p \lor (q.r)) \supset ((p \lor r)$ (3), (7), DR 1.
        $\supset ((p \lor q).(p \lor r)))$

(9) $((p \lor (q.r)) \supset ((p \lor r)$ D 30, $(p \lor (q.r)/p, (p \lor r)/q$
        $\supset (p \lor q).(p \lor r)))$ $((p \lor q).(p \lor r))/r$.
        $\supset ((p \lor r)$
        $\supset ((p \lor (q.r))$
        $\supset (p \lor q).(p \lor r)))$

(10) $(p \lor r) \supset ((p \lor (q.r))$ (8), (9), RST 3
         $\supset (p \lor q).(p \lor r))$

(11) $(p \lor (q.r)) \supset ((p \lor (q.r))$ (6), (10), DR 1.
         $\supset ((p \lor q).(p \lor r)))$

(12) $((p \lor (q.r)) \supset ((p \lor (q.r))$ D 29, $p \lor (q.r)/p$,
         $\supset ((p \lor q).(p \lor r))))$ $((p \lor q).(p \lor r))/q$.
         $\supset ((p \lor (q.r))$
         $\supset ((p \lor q).(p \lor r)))$

(13) $(p \lor (q.r))$ (11), (12), RST 3.
        $\supset ((p \lor q).(p \lor r))$

Given this result, the required equivalences present little difficulty. We have:

     D 32. $((p \lor q).(p \lor r)) \supset (p \lor (q.r))$.

     D 33. $(p \lor (q.r)) \equiv ((p \lor q).(p \lor r))$.

     D 34. $(p.(q \lor r)) \equiv ((p.q) \lor (p.r))$.

D 34 and D 33 are RF 12 and 13 respectively.

8. Completeness.   We now outline the method to be used for proving the completeness of AX. We shall prove completeness first in sense (1), that is to say, we shall prove that every tautology is a derivable formula of AX and therefore every extension of AX must result in the derivability of formulae which are not tautologies. For this purpose, we need the following results concerning tautologies:

THEOREM 6: Every tautology is reducible to a tautology in conjunctive normal form.

THEOREM 7: A formula in conjunctive normal form is a tautology if and only if every one of its component disjunctions is a tautology.

THEOREM 8: A disjunction is a tautology if and only if it contains at least one propositional variable and the negation of that variable.

These were established in Chapter III. Now we can prove the completeness of AX with the aid of Theorem 6 if we can prove the following:

I. Every tautological CNF is derivable in AX.

II. If any formula 'P' is reducible to a CNF derivable in AX, then 'P' is derivable in AX.

Given I and II, it is evident that the completeness of AX follows from Theorem 6.

We shall now investigate the conditions required for a proof of I. We can prove I with the aid of Theorem 7 if we can prove:

III. Every tautological disjunction is derivable in AX. By "disjunction" here, we mean, of course, a disjunction whose components are propositional variables or their negations. It is clear that, if III holds, then by the Rule of Adjunction (RST 4) every conjunction of tautological disjunctions is derivable in AX. And since by Theorem 7, every tautological CNF is a conjunction of tautological disjunctions, every tautological CNF will be derivable in AX. Now a tautological disjunction, with standard ordering can, by Theorem 8, and successive applications of D 9 and D 10 be transformed into:

$$((P \lor k) \lor \sim k) \lor Q$$

where 'P', 'Q' are disjunctions and 'k' is some propositional variable. So we have to show that all such formulae are derivable.

By D 11 (Section 7), '$p \lor \sim p$' is derivable, and so by RST 1, '$k \lor \sim k$' is derivable, whatever 'k' may be. By A 2, we have:

$$p \supset (q \lor p)$$

and so by RST 1:

$$(k \lor \sim k) \supset (P \lor (k \lor \sim k))$$

and by RST 3, '$P \lor (k \lor \sim k)$' is derivable. Now by D 10, we have

$$(p \lor (q \lor r)) \supset ((p \lor q) \lor r)$$

and by RST 1,

$$(P \lor (k \lor \sim k)) \supset ((P \lor k) \lor \sim k)$$

and again by RST 3, '$(P \lor k) \lor \sim k$' is derivable. Using A 2 and RST 1 again, we have:

$$((P \lor k) \lor \sim k) \supset Q \lor ((P \lor k) \lor \sim k)$$

and so, by RST 3, '$Q \lor ((P \lor k) \lor \sim k)$' is derivable; whence by A 3, RST 1 and 3, '$((P \lor k) \lor \sim k) \lor Q$' is derivable.

This proves:

THEOREM 9: Every tautological disjunction with standard ordering is derivable.

We then have:

THEOREM 10: Every tautological CNF is derivable. For since every one of its component disjuncts is derivable, so is the CNF by the Rule of Adjunction, RST 4.

We have now proved III (Theorem 9) and I (Theorem 10). It remains now only to prove II. This is a more complex matter and we must first reconsider the process of reduction. It will be remembered that this was carried out by replacing one expression by another according to certain reference formulae. For example, if we have the formula

'$p \supset (\sim \sim q \supset p)$', we are allowed to replace the occurrence of '$\sim \sim q$' in this formula by an occurrence of 'q', thus getting '$p \supset (q \supset p)$' and so on. Now such replacements result in equivalent formulae because the reference formula '$\sim \sim q \equiv q$' and its derivatives by substitution are *tautologies*. Furthermore, if the original formula '$p \supset (\sim \sim q \supset p)$' is a tautology, the formula obtained from it is also a tautology. In general, we have:

IV. If '$Q \equiv R$' is a tautology and if '$P(Q)$' is a formula containing 'Q' and if '$P(R)$' is the result of putting 'R' for an occurrence of 'Q' in '$P(Q)$', then '$P(Q) \equiv P(R)$' is a tautology.

V. If '$Q \equiv R$' is a tautology and '$P(Q)$' is a tautology, so is '$P(R)$' and conversely.

Evidently V follows from IV and the fact that IV preserves equivalence is the fact that validates reduction by RF 7-17.

Now we have to prove something parallel to IV only with "is derivable" for "is a tautology". Then we can show that if 'P' is reducible to 'Q', and 'Q' is derivable, so is 'P'. This will give us II.

We now prove the statement got by putting "is derivable" for "is a tautology" in IV. In other words:

THEOREM 11 (*Replacement Theorem*): If '$Q \equiv R$' is derivable and if '$P(R)$' is got from '$P(Q)$' by putting 'R' for 'Q' in '$P(Q)$' then '$P(Q) \equiv P(R)$' is derivable.

We prove the theorem in three parts:

Part 1. The theorem holds in the case of propositional variables. For if '$P(Q)$' is a propositional variable, '$P(Q)$' is the same as 'Q' and '$P(R)$' must be the same as 'R', so '$P(Q) \equiv P(R)$' is the same formula as '$Q \equiv R$'.

Part 2. If the theorem holds for any formula '$P(Q)$' it holds also for '$\sim P(Q)$'. Since the theorem holds for '$P(Q)$', we have '$Q \equiv R \vdash P(Q) \equiv P(R)$'.

By D 28, $\qquad (P(Q) \equiv P(R)) \supset (P(Q) \supset P(R))$

and by D 19, $\quad (P(Q) \supset P(R)) \supset (\sim P(R) \supset \sim P(Q))$

and by DR 1, $\quad P(Q) \equiv P(R)) \supset (\sim P(R) \supset \sim P(Q)).$

Likewise, $\qquad (P(Q) \equiv P(R)) \supset (\sim P(Q) \supset \sim P(R)).$

Hence, $\qquad Q \equiv R \vdash \sim P(Q) \supset \sim P(R),$
$$\sim P(R) \supset \ \sim P(Q).$$

So by DR 2, $\quad Q \equiv R \vdash \sim P(Q) \equiv \ \sim P(R).$

Part 3. If the theorem holds for '$P(Q)$', '$S(Q)$', it holds also for '$P(Q) \lor S(Q)$'.

Since the theorem holds for '$P(Q)$', '$S(Q)$', we have:

$$Q \equiv R \vdash P(Q) \equiv P(R), \ S(Q) \equiv S(R).$$

So using D 28, DR 1, $\quad Q \equiv R \vdash P(Q) \supset P(R), P(R) \supset P(Q)$
$$Q \equiv R \vdash S(Q) \supset S(R), S(R) \supset S(Q).$$

By A 4, RST 3, $\quad Q \equiv R \vdash (P(Q) \lor S(Q)) \supset (P(R) \lor S(Q))$
$$Q \equiv R \vdash (P(R) \lor S(Q)) \supset (P(R) \lor S(R)).$$

So by DR 1, $\quad Q \equiv R \vdash (P(Q) \lor S(Q)) \supset (P(R) \lor S(R)).$

Likewise, $\qquad Q \equiv R \vdash (P(R) \lor S(R)) \supset (P(Q) \lor S(Q)).$

And by DR 2, $\quad Q \equiv R \vdash (P(Q) \lor S(Q)) \equiv (P(R) \lor S(R)).$

Since all formulae can be built up from propositional variables, '$\lor$' and '$\sim$', introducing '$\supset$' and '.' by definition where necessary, the theorem must hold for all formulae.

The equivalent of V then follows:

THEOREM 12: If '$Q \equiv R$' is derivable, and '$P(R)$' is derivable, then '$P(Q)$' is also derivable.

To complete our proof of II, we have only to show that all the reference formulae 7-17, which are tautologies, are also derivable. This has already been done in Section 7. Thus:

THEOREM 13: If any formula 'P' is reducible to a CNF derivable in AX, then 'P' is derivable in AX.

From Theorems 6, 10, and 13 we have:

THEOREM 14: Every tautology is derivable in AX.

We have already shown that all derivable formulae are tautologies (in connection with consistency). Therefore:

THEOREM 15: The class of derivable formulae in AX is identical with the class of tautologies.

The completeness of a set of axioms may be explained in two ways. (i) An axiom set is complete if it forms a sufficient basis for proving *all* the tautologies of the system. It has already been proved that AX is complete in this sense. (ii) The second (and stronger) sense of "completeness" is this: a set of axioms is complete if the addition of another *independent* axiom makes the set inconsistent.

We can prove as follows that AX is complete in sense (ii) also. Suppose that 'P' is any WFF which cannot be proved from the axioms. Then this expression will have a conjunctive normal form (CNF) which we may call 'Q'. 'Q' will be of the form '$R_1 . R_2 . R_3 . \ldots . R_n$' where the R's are disjunctions of negated and unnegated propositional variables. But since 'P' and, therefore, 'Q' are not provable from the axioms, *at least one* of the R's must contain *no mutually contradictory components*. Call this disjunction 'R_k'. We may perform a uniform substitution on 'R_k' in accordance with RST 1. We shall substitute 'p' for every propositional variable which is not negated and '$\sim p$' for every *negated* propositional variable. For example, if 'R_k' is:

$$(p \lor \sim q \lor r \lor \sim s)$$

our substitution gives:

$$(p \lor \sim \sim p \lor p \lor \sim \sim p).$$

And this, in turn, is equivalent to '$(p \lor p \lor p \lor p)$' which is equivalent to 'p'.

But if 'P' is supposed to be a valid formula, then 'Q' and, therefore, 'R_k' will be valid formulas. And since 'R_k' can be written by substitution as 'p', 'p' will be a valid formula. And this cannot possibly be the case, because by another equally permissible substitution in accordance with RST 1, we can write '$\sim p$' for every unnegated propositional variable in 'R_k' and 'p' for every negated variable giving:

$$(\sim p \lor \sim p \lor \sim p \lor \sim p)$$

which is equivalent to '$\sim p$'. Thus the supposition that 'P' cannot be proved from the axioms and is nevertheless a valid formula leads to the conclusion that both 'p' and '$\sim p$' are valid formulas. And this is a contradiction. Thus A 1-4 are complete in the sense that if any independent axiom is added to them, a contradiction will result. [The reader should verify for himself that a similar pair of substitutions cannot be made in an axiom of AX (or in a theorem following from the axioms) consistently with RST 1.]

BIBLIOGRAPHICAL NOTE

CHAPTER IV

A clear elementary account of the axiomatic development of the propositional calculus will be found in Ambrose and Lazerowitz (1), but no proofs of consistency, completeness, and independence are given. An excellent elementary discussion from a more general point of view is given in Tarski (31). The classical treatment will again be found in Hilbert and Ackermann (12). Eaton (10) gives a simple introduction to the axiom system of *Principia Mathematica* (33).

CHAPTER V

ELEMENTS OF THE PREDICATE CALCULUS

1. Some New Forms of Inference. There are many quite simple forms of inference, which are clearly valid, but whose validity cannot be established by the methods of truth-functional analysis which we have been examining in Chapters II and III. Here are some examples:

(1) All ordinary members of the society pay an annual subscription of one guinea, and all who pay an annual subscription of one guinea receive the publications of the society without further charge. Consequently, all ordinary members of the society receive the publications of the society without further charge.

(2) All missionaries have rigid views on morals, and no one with rigid views on morals makes a good anthropologist. Therefore, no missionaries make good anthropologists.

(3) All undergraduates have the right to use the university library and some undergraduates are not seriously interested in scholarship. Consequently, some who have the right to use the university library are not seriously interested in scholarship.

It will be noticed that the validity of these inferences seems to depend in some way on the uses of the words "all", "some", "none", and equivalent expressions and on the way in which certain *descriptive* phrases (such as "ordinary member", "pays an annual subscription of one guinea", and the like) serve to link together the premisses and the conclusion. It is clear that arguments of this sort will not be valid unless the linking of premisses to conclusion satisfies certain conditions. It must therefore be our aim to specify these conditions correctly. We hope thereby to obtain a mechanical procedure for testing such arguments and this will be useful in more complicated arguments where intuition is not an infallible guide. Such a mechanical procedure will, of course, be a *decision method* analogous to the method of truth-tables or normal forms which we have described in previous chapters.

It may be useful here, in order to bring out the essential character of the arguments with which we shall now be concerned, to refer back to the two examples which were discussed at the beginning of the second chapter.

(4) All dangerous trades should be highly paid and mining is a dangerous trade. Therefore, mining should be highly paid.

(5) If mining is a dangerous trade, then it should be highly paid. Mining is a dangerous trade. Therefore, mining should be highly paid.

We saw that the subject-matter of these two arguments is the same and that they have an identical conclusion. Nevertheless, they are, from the point of view of logic, fundamentally different in character. In the case of (5), we can ignore the structure of the propositions "mining is a dangerous trade" and "mining should be highly paid" and test the validity of the corresponding logical skeleton:

(6) $((p \supset q).p) \supset q.$

But we cannot do the same in the case of (4). The logical structure of the argument, if we pay attention only to the propositions involved and not to the *descriptive terms* of which the propositions are composed, would be:

(7) $(p.q) \supset r.$

Now this is clearly *not* a valid form. That is to say, an argument of this form is not valid *simply* in virtue of being of this form. Thus it is obvious that our failure to take account of the internal structure of the propositions of (4), viz. "All dangerous trades should be highly paid", and so on, has led to our missing the essential logical point of the argument. If therefore we are to give an account of the validity of arguments of the type "All A's are B's and x is an A; therefore, x is a B" we shall have to look into the *structure* of those propositions which we have hitherto taken as unanalysed units.

2. Singular Propositions. If, therefore, we are to fulfil our programme, it is essential that we now consider the analysis of propositions into elements *which are not themselves propositions*. This is in striking contrast to our former procedure where propositions were regarded either as compounded from other propositions or as irreducible elements. We start with the very simplest kind of proposition, the *singular proposition*. A singular proposition may be defined negatively as one which does not contain truth-functional connectives (logical constants) and which also is free from such words as "all", "none", "some", and their equivalents. Here are some examples of singular propositions:

(1) Smith is bald.

(2) Smith is older than Jones.

(3) Reading is between Oxford and London.

It is clear that the result of analysing these propositions will not be other propositions but something else which we shall call generally *terms*. Example (1) contains two terms, "Smith" and "bald". Example (2) has *three* terms, "Smith", "Jones", and "older than"; **(3)** has *four* terms, "Reading", "Oxford", "London", and "between". And we can imagine propositions containing more than four terms, although they are not very common in practice. In any case, we shall be concerned in this chapter only with singular propositions containing just *two* terms like proposition (1). The more complicated singular propositions introduce complexities which are not well suited to an elementary discussion.

Let us now have some more examples of singular propositions containing just two terms:

(4) (Smith) is (bald).

(5) (London) is (the largest city).

(6) (Mr Churchill) is (the present prime minister of Great Britain).

(7) (Italy) is (a country with a warm climate).

In each case we have marked off the two terms. And it will be seen that, in each case, one of these terms is a *proper name* and the other term is a *descriptive word or phrase*. The proper name is said to be the *logical subject* of the proposition and the descriptive word or phrase is called the *logical predicate*. (The reader will notice that these terms are adapted from the technical terms of grammar. There are, however, considerable differences between logical and grammatical subjects and logical and grammatical predicates, and it should never be assumed that the logical subject of a given proposition is the same as the grammatical subject of the corresponding sentence or that the logical predicate of a given proposition is the same as the grammatical predicate of the corresponding sentence. This will, in fact, by no means always be so.) It is clear from the examples given that a singular proposition says that a certain object, specified by a proper name, satisfies a certain description. And the proposition will be true if and only if the object does in fact satisfy the description.

In the sequel, we shall often require to make statements which will be true of any arbitrarily given singular propositions. We shall therefore use such letters as '*a*', '*b*',

'c' (or 'a_1', 'a_2', 'a_3', . . .) to stand for arbitrary proper names and the letters 'f', 'g', 'h' to stand for arbitrary predicates. The letters 'a', 'b', 'c', which stand in this way for proper names, will be called *individual constants*. The letters 'f', 'g', 'h', . . . will be called *predicate constants*. Arbitrary singular propositions will then be symbolised by such combinations 'fa', 'ga', 'fb', and so on. We shall therefore understand the symbolic expression 'fa' to be read as:

"a has the property f",

where 'a' is understood to be functioning as a proper name.

These combinations of letters and some others to be introduced later are called *predicate formulae*. (We shall refer to them, for short, as *formulae* where, as usually in the present chapter, there is no danger of confusing them with the *propositional formulae* discussed in previous chapters.) These formulae may be interpreted as standing for *any* singular propositions, according to the meanings which we choose to assign to the letters 'a', 'b', 'f', 'g', etc. Thus it is impossible to discuss the truth or falsity of a *formula*. It is only when we *interpret* the individual constant 'a' and the predicate constant 'f' of the formula 'fa' that we can assign the value "true" or "false". And then we shall be speaking of the *proposition* which results from giving this interpretation to the 'a' and the 'f' of 'fa'. For example, if we interpret 'a' as "London" and 'f' as "a large city" we get the true proposition "London is a large city". Once the interpretation is known, the truth-value can, in general, be assigned but it is an important property of some formulae that they may come out true under one interpretation and false under another. For example, in the example given above, 'fa' takes the value "true" if we interpret 'a' as "London" and 'f' as "is a large city" but takes the value "false" if we read 'a' as "London" and 'f' as "is a small town".

The reader may be a little puzzled by the fact that 'f', 'a' are called *constants*, when 'fa' can be interpreted to mean any singular proposition that we choose. The reason is that the term "individual variable" is required to mean something quite different as will become clear in Sections 5 and 6. The matter is discussed more fully in Section 9. A point to be noticed is that the use of the term "variable" in the predicate calculus is subject to restrictions which are not applicable to the more intuitive sense of the word already introduced in the phrase "propositional variable" in Chapters II, III, and IV.

3. Further Remarks on Proper Names and Descriptions. The distinction between proper names and descriptions has been the subject of a good deal of *philosophical* discussion. Fortunately the objects and results of this discussion are almost entirely irrelevant to the study of elementary logic. For our purposes, anything which is grammatically a proper name is also logically a proper name. But there are one or two possible confusions which we should guard ourselves against.

The first point to make clear is that propositions like "A man is bald" or "Some man is bald" or "The horse is a noble animal" are *not* singular propositions, because they contain no proper name. They are, in fact, in spite of their simple appearance, complex propositions of a type which we shall discuss in their proper place. The second point is that, although a proper name is uniquely assigned (that is, in the course of a particular argument it must be used to refer to one and only one individual), this is not a defining characteristic of proper names. Some descriptions, as, for example, "the present queen of England", can, of their nature, describe one and only one individual. They are, nevertheless, *descriptions* and not proper names. We can bring out the difference between these uniquely descriptive phrases and true proper names by pointing out that some descriptions of this type do not *describe anyone or anything*. Consider, for example, the phrase "the present king of France". A proper name, on the other hand, must refer to an individual.

If we require some further insight into the difference between a proper name and a description, we may consider the following example. The word "Palumbo" is a proper name. But if you knew that you were going to see Palumbo to-morrow, you would not know at all what to expect. It might be a man, a horse, a dog, a mountain, a river, a city, or numberless other things. The name "Palumbo" does not give you the smallest clue as to the nature of the thing named. In other words, it is not descriptive.

4. Relations between the Propositional Calculus and the Predicate Calculus. It is important to realise that our transition from the logic of unanalysed propositions to the logic of predicates does not involve a sharp break with our previous methods of treatment. The predicate calculus is based on the propositional calculus and uses its methods and its notation so far as these are applicable to the new types of logical structure with which it has to deal. The propositional formula '$p \lor q$' represents a compound proposition which is composed of *any* two simple propositions united by the word "or" taken in its inclusive sense. It might represent any of the following propositions (1)-(6) or any of an indefinite number of others of the same form:

(1) Either all men are mortal or twice two are five.

(2) Either Reading is between Oxford and London or twice two are five.

(3) Either Jones is dishonest or some accountants are careless.

(4) Either Jones is dishonest or Jones is foolish.

(5) Either Jones is dishonest or Smith is dishonest.

(6) Either Jones is dishonest or Smith is mistaken.

Suppose, however, we replace the compound propositional formula '$p \vee q$' by the predicate formula '$fa \vee ga$'. This certainly stands for a disjunction of propositions but not for a disjunction of *any two* propositions as does '$p \vee q$'. It stands only for a disjunction of any two *singular* propositions with the same logical subject but different predicates. Of the examples (1)-(6) above, it therefore represents only (4). We could similarly represent (5), which is a disjunction of two singular propositions with the same predicate but different subjects by '$fa \vee fb$'. And example (6) which is a disjunction of two singular propositions differing in both subject *and* predicate would be symbolised by '$fa \vee gb$'. But examples (1), (2), and (3) above each contain as a term in the disjunction at least one simple proposition which is not a singular proposition. [For example, "some accountants are careless" in (3).] They cannot therefore be symbolised with the logical apparatus so far at our disposal other than as *unanalysed* propositional units in the formula '$p \vee q$'.

It will be seen therefore that predicate formulae of the type 'fa', 'fb', 'gb', . . . stand for propositions just as do 'p', 'q', 'r', . . . in the propositional calculus. The only difference is that the predicate formulae give some idea of the *internal structure* of the propositions for which they stand while the propositional formulae do not. We may thus use in developing the calculus of predicates the apparatus of logical constants and brackets which we have used so far in the logic of propositions.

For example, the formula :

$$((p \supset q).(\sim r \supset \sim q)) \supset (p \supset r)$$

is a valid formula of the propositional calculus. Similarly,

$$((fa \supset ga).(\sim fb \supset \sim ga)) \supset (fa \supset fb)$$

is a valid formula of the calculus of predicates. The difference between the two is merely that the second gives us the additional information (i) that the propositions involved are all singular propositions; (ii) that the first two propositions have the same subject but different predicates and the third proposition has the same predicate as the first but a different subject.

We may thus regard the calculus of predicates as a branch of logic which includes the calculus of propositions but goes beyond it. It includes it in the sense that, if any formula is valid in the calculus of propositions, the corresponding predicate formula will be valid in the predicate calculus. But it goes beyond it in the sense that it makes the *structure* of its propositional material explicit. And because of this it is able to deal with forms of argument which, on account of their complexity, are beyond the scope of the propositional calculus.

5. The Particular Quantifier: Existence.

Consider the following propositions:

(1) Centaurs exist.

(2) Horses exist.

These are not singular propositions, since they contain no proper names. On the other hand, the word "exist" can hardly be called a description. The assertion that horses exist does not tell you what kind of things horses are. How, then, are such propositions to be analysed?

Now let us consider the two sentences:

(3) There is something which is a centaur.

(4) There is something which is a horse.

Clearly, these two sentences express exactly the same propositions as the first two, though the form of expression is, perhaps, less usual. Now we can split (3) and (4) each into two parts as follows:

(5) (There is something) (which is a centaur).

(6) (There is something) (which is a horse).

This phrase "there is something" expresses one of the fundamental concepts of logic and it is not capable of further analysis. It is called the *particular quantifier* (or, alternatively, the *existential quantifier*). The relative pronoun "which" is also fundamental and we shall see that the part it plays in logic is something like the part played by a variable in elementary algebra. In fact, we use the letters '*x*', '*y*', '*z*' in logic in place of the written word "which" and also in place of the word "something". Thus (5) and (6) become:

(7) (There is an *x*) (*x* is a centaur).

(8) (There is an *x*) (*x* is a horse).

Now using the arbitrary letters '*f*' and '*g*' as predicate symbols, we put '*f*' for "is a centaur" in (7) and '*g*' for "is a horse" in (8):

(9) (There is an *x*) (*fx*).

(10) (There is an *x*) (*gx*).

Lastly, we introduce the symbol '∃' for "there is an" getting:

(11) (∃*x*) (*fx*).

(12) (∃*x*) (*gx*).

These expressions show the logical structure of propositions like "centaurs exist" and "horses exist" and it is upon this structure that the logical properties of these propositions depend.

It may perhaps appear, at first sight, that the introduction of this rather elaborate symbolic apparatus to express a simple proposition like "horses exist" is pedantic and unnecessary. This is, however, not the case. The discovery of the correct analysis of existential propositions and the devising of a logical symbolism which makes their structure explicit has had important results both in logic and in philosophy. Some of the logical virtues of this symbolism will become clear as we proceed.

6. Analysis of some Quantified Propositions. Suppose we want to say:

(1) Centaurs do not exist.

Obviously, this is merely the negation of "Centaurs exist", and will thus have the form:

(2) $\sim (\exists x)$ (x is a centaur)

or (3) $\sim (\exists x)$ (fx).

Now consider:

(4) Some centaurs are vindictive.

This becomes:

(5) (There is something) (which is a centaur and which is vindictive).

And putting 'f' for "is a centaur" and 'g' for "is vindictive", we have:

(6) $(\exists x)$ ($fx.gx$).

Similarly:

(7) No centaurs are vindictive

becomes:

(8) $\sim$ (Some centaurs are vindictive)

which has the form:

(9) $\sim (\exists x)$ ($fx.gx$).

Likewise:

(10) All centaurs are vindictive

may be rewritten:

(11) No centaurs are not vindictive

which has the form:

(12) $\sim (\exists x)\ (fx.\sim gx)$.

It must be noticed, in connection with expressions like (6), that

(6) $(\exists x)\ (fx.gx)$

is *not* the same as:

(13) $(\exists x)\ (fx).(\exists x)\ (gx)$.

With the meanings at present assigned to 'f' and 'g', (6) means:

(4) Some centaurs are vindictive,

whereas (13) says that something is a centaur and something (*which may or may not be the same thing*) is vindictive. That is to say, (13) means the same as:

(14) Centaurs exist and vindictive things exist.

And this might very well be true even if no centaurs were vindictive.

It must again be stressed that formulae like '$(\exists x)\ (fx)$', '$(\exists x)\ (fx.gx)$', and so on, may be interpreted to stand for many different propositions. (In fact, any one of these formulae may be interpreted in an indefinitely large number of ways.) It is an important property of some such formulae, that under some interpretations they express a true proposition and under others a false one. There are other formulae, such as '$(\exists x)\ (fx \vee \sim fx)$', which clearly must come out true, *no matter what* meaning we assign to 'f'. The only condition for the truth of such a formula is that *something*, no matter what, should exist. Likewise, there are other formulae, such as '$(\exists x)\,(fx.\sim fx)$', which must be *false* no matter what meaning we assign to 'f'. (The reader will notice that these three classes of predicate formulae are precisely analogous to the contingent, tautological, and contravalid formulae of the propositional calculus.)

All the formulae which we have discussed so far, with the exception of (13) above, are *simple quantified formulae*. That is to say, they consist of a *single* quantifier followed by an open* formula, such as 'fx', '$fx \lor gx$', and so on. For the present we shall confine our attention to such formulae, taking up the more complex forms again in Sections 10 and 11.

7. The Universal Quantifier.   The proposition:

(1) Centaurs exist

may be expressed, as far as concerns its logical structure, in the form:

(2) There is an x such that x is a centaur,

or   (3) $(\exists x)\,(fx)$.

The proposition:

(4) Centaurs do not exist

is clearly the negation of (1) and has the form:

(5) $\sim (\exists x)\,(fx)$.

But (4) may be expressed as:

(6) Nothing is a centaur

or   (7) Whatever x may be, x is not a centaur.

The form of expression "whatever x may be" is called the *universal quantifier* and is expressed symbolically by

* For a more detailed explanation of "open formulae", see Section 9 below.

'(x)'. Hence the logical structure of (7) may be expressed as:

(8) $(x)(\sim fx)$.

The proposition:

(9) Everything is a centaur

has the form:

(10) $(x)(fx)$.

Evidently, then (5) and (8) have the same meaning and, in a sense, the universal quantifier is superfluous. It can be defined in terms of '$(\exists x)$' and '$\sim$' just as the constant '.' can be defined in terms of '$\lor$' and '$\sim$'. But, of course, we might just as well have introduced the universal quantifier first and defined the particular quantifier in terms of it. We can have either:

    (a) '$(x) A$' is defined to mean '$\sim (\exists x) \sim A$'

or (b) '$(\exists x) A$' is defined to mean '$\sim (x) \sim A$'.

[We shall use expressions of the form '$(x) A$', '$(\exists x) B$', and so on, as abbreviations for ordinary quantified expressions. The capital letters 'A', 'B', . . . will therefore stand for simple or complex open formulae of the type 'fx', '$fx \supset gx$', etc.]

Whichever we choose, it is clear that where 'A' is a truth-function of expressions like 'fx', 'gx', etc., we can always write '$(x) A$' in place of '$\sim (\exists x) \sim A$' or '$(\exists x) A$' in place of '$\sim (x) \sim A$'. And analogously, we can always put '$(x) \sim A$' in place of '$\sim (\exists x) A$' and '$(\exists x) \sim A$' in place of '$\sim (x) A$'. Thus if negation signs appear in front of a simple quantified formula, we can always eliminate them, first by the rule for striking out double negations and secondly by the rules given here. For this reason, the introduction of *two* quantifiers greatly simplifies our treatment of simple quantified formulae.

8. The Interpretation of Quantifiers as Conjunctions and Disjunctions. The reader may have noticed, especially in view of the analogy cited above, a certain similarity of logical behaviour between the particular and the universal quantifiers on the one hand and the logical constants '$\vee$' and '$.$' on the other. Just as de Morgan's rules enable us to transform propositional formulae of the type '$P.Q$' into '$\sim(\sim P \vee \sim Q)$' and '$P \vee Q$' into '$\sim(\sim P.\sim Q)$', so there is a corresponding duality between '$(\exists x)$' and '(x)', so that they can be defined in terms of one another with the help of the negation sign.

This may be made clearer by considering the relations between quantified formulae and certain conjunctions and disjunctions of singular formulae as follows. We have seen that:

(1) Centaurs exist

may be rewritten without change of meaning as:

(2) (There is an x) (x is a centaur).

Now (1) and (2) assert that *at least one thing* has the property of being a centaur. Consequently (1) and (2) are true if and only if:

(3) Either a_1 is a centaur *or* a_2 is a centaur *or* a_3 is a centaur *or* . . . *or* a_n is a centaur

is true, where a_1, a_2, . . . a_n are all the individuals in the universe. Thus:

(4) $(\exists x)\,(fx)$

will be true if and only if

(5) $fa_1 \vee fa_2 \vee fa_3 \vee \ldots \vee fa_n$

is true. We have thus obtained a relation between the particular quantifier and the logical constant '$\vee$'.

Similarly, to assert a universal proposition such as:

(6) Everything is material

is to assert something which will be true if and only if (7) is true.

(7) a_1 is material *and* a_2 is material *and* . . . *and* a_n is material,

where a_1, a_2, . . . a_n as before are all the things in the universe.

We should express (6) symbolically as:

(8) $(x)(fx)$

and (7) symbolically as:

(9) $fa_1.fa_2.fa_3. \ldots .fa_n$,

thus obtaining a relation between the universal quantifier and a *conjunction*.

We shall call (5) and (9) the *propositional expansions* of (4) and (8) respectively.

Now we know from the rules of the propositional calculus that:

(10) $(fa_1 \lor fa_2 \lor \ldots \lor fa_n) \equiv \sim(\sim fa_1.\sim fa_2. \ldots .\sim fa_n)$.

(11) $(fa_1.fa_2. \ldots .fa_n) \equiv \sim(\sim fa_1 \lor \sim fa_2 \lor \ldots \lor \sim fa_n)$.

And we saw above that, if $a_1 \ldots a_n$ represent all the objects in the universe, the left-hand side of (10) is true if and only if

(12) $(\exists x)(fx)$

is true. Furthermore (12) is equivalent to:

(13) $\sim(x)(\sim fx)$

and (13) is true if and only if the right-hand side of (10) is true. Similarly, the left-hand side of (11) is true if and only if

(14) $(x)(fx)$

is true. And (14) is the same as:

(15) $\sim(\exists x)(\sim fx)$

which is true if and only if the right-hand side of (11) is true. Thus the duality of the quantifiers '(x)' and '$(\exists x)$' is a consequence of the de Morgan rules which are laws of the propositional calculus.

It is important to note that this relation between quantified formulae and certain conjunctions and disjunctions holds in general only when the number of individuals concerned is *finite*. But we do not need to consider the possibility of infinite domains of individuals at this stage. (See Chapter VI, Section 6.)

9. Free and Bound Variables: Constants. A certain amount of confusion is apt to arise in students' minds about the use of the terms "constant" and "variable" in logic. A few words of explanation will therefore be useful at this stage. In the part of logic with which this chapter deals, we employ just *six* different kinds of symbols:

(1) Individual constants: $a, b, c, \ldots$

(2) Individual variables: $x, y, z \ldots$

(3) Predicate constants: $f, g, h, \ldots$

(4) Quantifiers: $(x), (\exists x), (y), (\exists y), \ldots$

(5) Connectives (or Logical Constants): $\sim, V, ., \supset, \equiv.$

(6) Brackets: $(,)$.

Starting with these, we define a class of *well-formed* (or *meaningful*) *formulae*, as follows:

(i) If 'α' is a predicate constant and 'β' an individual constant, or an individual variable, then '$\alpha\beta$' is a well-formed formula (or WFF, for short).

(ii) If 'A' is a WFF, so is '$\sim (A)$'.

(iii) If 'A' and 'B' are WFF's, so are '$(A).(B)$', '$(A) V (B)$', and so on.

(iv) If 'A' is a WFF containing a *free* individual variable
'α', then '(α) A', '(∃α) A' are WFF's.

By "a formula containing a free individual variable",
we mean a formula like '*fx*', or '(*y*) (*fy* ⊃ *gx*)', where
there occurs a variable (in these cases '*x*') which is not
preceded by an appropriate quantifier. Such formulae
are called *open formulae* and are contrasted with *closed
formulae* which do not contain any free variables. A
bound variable is one which is preceded by a suitable
quantifier. Thus in '(*y*) (*fy* ⊃ *gx*)', '*y*' is a bound variable
and '*x*' is a free variable.

When we speak of truth or falsity in logic, we usually
mean the *logical* truth (or validity) and *logical* falsity (or
contravalidity or contradiction). In Chapter II, we
discussed this kind of truth and falsity in its relation to the
logic of propositions. But if we want to use the words
"truth" and "falsity" in their ordinary sense, we can do
so only by giving rules so that our formulae (or some of
them) can be interpreted to stand for *propositions*. Then
we shall say that a formula is true if and only if the proposition which it is interpreted to stand for is true. *We
interpret a formula by assigning meanings to the constants
in it.* Thus we might let '*a*' mean the individual John and
'*f*' mean the property of being tall. Then we have given
to the formula '*fa*' the meaning that John is tall. And
'*fa*' will be true if and only if John is tall. Of course, we
could interpret '*fa*' to mean something quite different;
the important thing is that once we have assigned a particular meaning to a formula in a given context, we must
stick to it.

The difference between constants and variables now
becomes clear.

(1) Constants cannot be quantified.

(2) *We cannot interpret*, i.e. *assign, a meaning to a variable.*

For this latter reason, formulae which contain free variables cannot strictly be said to be true or false. Consider, for example, the difference between '*fa*' and '*fx*'. Suppose '*a*' means "the number five" and '*f*' means "odd". Then '*fa*' says that the number five is odd, which is in fact the case. So '*fa*' is true under this interpretation. But '*fx*' simply says that *x* is odd; and this is neither true nor false.* We can, of course, say if we wish that "*x* is odd" is true *for some values of x* and false for others.

The fact is that in logic we are not really very interested (at this stage) in particular interpretations of formulae. This is because we are not, as logicians, much interested in *factual* or empirical truth; we are interested rather in logical truth. One of the main purposes of an exposition of logic is to give a clear meaning to the phrase "logical truth". And we propose as at least a partial explication of "logical truth" the following:

A formula is logically true if and only if it is true *no matter what interpretation we give* to the constant terms in it.

This is essentially nothing but a clearer restatement of the old doctrine that valid inference is independent of subject-matter. (See Chapter I.) But it is not put forward as a final definition or last word, so to speak. It just happens to suffice for the present.

The other important point for the student to notice is that the notion of logical truth (as distinct from factual

---

* Expressions like "*x* is odd", "*x* is red", and so on, are often referred to as "propositional functions". A propositional function was defined by Lord Russell, who introduced the term, as "an expression containing one or more undetermined constituents such that, when values are assigned to these constituents, the expression becomes a proposition". (*Introduction to Mathematical Philosophy*, pp. 155-6.) Because of certain technicalities connected with the use of the term "propositional function" in Russell's logic, the term is perhaps best avoided in an elementary discussion.

truth) is extended to include open formulae. This is done by saying that an open formula is logically true if and only if its universal closure is logically true. That is to say, '$fx \supset fx$' is logically true because '(x) $(fx \supset fx)$' is so; and '(y) $(fy \supset gx)$' is not logically true because '(x) (y) $(fy \supset gx)$' is not logically true.

10. Interpretation and Satisfiable Formulae. A singular formula, like 'fa', can be interpreted to stand for a true proposition or a false one. For example, if we give 'a' the meaning "Socrates" and 'f' the meaning "is mortal", then 'fa' will represent the true proposition "Socrates is mortal". If we make 'a' mean "Plato" and 'f' mean "is alive to-day", then 'fa' has the meaning "Plato is alive to-day" which is false. Thus any singular formula may stand for a true proposition and we express this by saying:

I. *Any singular formula is satisfiable.*

If now we consider truth-functions of singular formulae, it is easy to see that these will be satisfiable if and only if the truth-function is not contradictory. For if the truth-function is not contradictory, there will be some interpretation of the singular formulae in it which will make the function true. For example, suppose that the function we are considering is:

(1) $(fa \lor fb) \supset gc$.

Interpreting 'a', 'b', and 'c' by "Socrates", "Plato", and "Aristotle" respectively and the predicate variables 'f' and 'g' by "mortal" and "intelligent" we get:

(2) If Socrates is mortal or Plato is mortal then Aristotle is intelligent.

Analysing the truth-values of (2) we get:

$$((1 \lor 1) \supset 1) = (1 \supset 1) = 1.$$

Similarly, it is clear that we cannot make a *contradictory* function true, no matter what meanings we assign to the singular formulae. No interpretation can make:

(3) $fa . \sim fa$

come out true. For if 'fa' is true, '$\sim fa$' is always false and vice versa. And a conjunction cannot be true unless *both* components are true. Thus contradictory truth-functions will always be *unsatisfiable*. We therefore have:

II. *A truth-function of singular formulae is satisfiable if and only if it is not contradictory.*

Let us now consider formulae like '$(\exists x)(fx)$', '$(\exists x)(fx \lor gx)$', etc., which contain just one particular quantifier. We know that '$(\exists x)(fx)$', for example, means that there exists an object having the property 'f' and this will be true if and only if some singular formula of the type 'fa' is true. Likewise, '$(\exists x)(fx \lor gx)$' will be true if and only if some interpretation of the formula '$fa \lor ga$' is true. We have seen that where we have a formula of the type '$(\exists x) A$' (in which the individual variables are bound by a single particular quantifier), it can be expanded into an equivalent disjunction of singular propositions (or truth-functions of such propositions). For example:

(4) $(\exists x)(fx . \sim gx)$

can be expanded as:

(5) $(fa_1 . \sim ga_1) \lor (fa_2 . \sim ga_2) \lor \ldots \lor (fa_n . \sim ga_n)$.

Formulae of the type '$(\exists x) A$' will therefore be satisfiable if and only if their propositional expansion is not contradictory. For instance:

(6) $(\exists x)(fx . \sim fx)$

is expanded as:

(7) $(fa_1 . \sim fa_1) \lor (fa_2 . \sim fa_2) \lor \ldots \lor (fa_n . \sim fa_n)$

which is clearly contradictory. Thus (6) is *not* satisfiable. We therefore have:

III. *Formulae of the type '($\exists x$) A' whose individual variables are bound by a single existential quantifier are satisfiable if and only if their propositional expansions are not contradictory.*

Lastly, we have formulae like '(x) A' whose propositional expansions are *conjunctions* of the form:

(8) $P_1.P_2.P_3. \ldots .P_n$

where the P's are singular propositions (of the type 'fa') or truth-functions of such singular propositions. Such a formula as '(x) A' says that *everything* satisfies the conditions 'A'. That is to say, '(x) A' is true if and only if the result of putting 'a' for 'x' throughout 'A' is a true proposition, no matter what 'a' is taken to refer to. Suppose, for example, we have the formula

(9) $(x) (fx)$.

Granted that there is some property which is possessed by everything in the universe and 'f' is interpreted to stand for that property, then 'fa' will be true, no matter what meaning we assign to 'a'. If 'A' is some molecular open formula such as:

(10) $(fx \supset gx)$ ∨ hx,

by putting 'a' for 'x' we get:

(11) $(fa \supset ga)$ ∨ ha.

And this will be true for certain truth-values of the components, for example: $((1 \supset 1)$ ∨ $0) = (1$ ∨ $0) = 1$. For we can arrange for (11) to be true, no matter what 'a' refers to, by choosing suitable meanings for 'f', 'g', and 'h'. Thus:

(12) $(x) ((fx \supset gx)$ ∨ $hx)$

will be satisfiable. In general:

IV. '(x) A' *is satisfiable if its propositional expansion is not contradictory.*

11. Simultaneously Satisfiable Formulae. A pair of formulae 'A' and 'B' are *simultaneously satisfiable* if we can assign meanings to the predicate constants and the individual constants (if any) in 'A' and 'B', so that both 'A' and 'B' express true propositions. (Of course, if the same letter, for example '*f*', appears in both 'A' and 'B' it must bear the same interpretation in both cases.)

Turning to the simple kind of quantified formulae which we have been considering, we see that there are just three possible kinds of pairs:

  (i) '(x) A'; '(x) B'.

  (ii) '(x) A'; '$(\exists x)$ B'.

  (iii) '$(\exists x)$ A'; '$(\exists x)$ B'.

[The case of '$(\exists x)$ A' and '(x) B' is obviously the same as (2).]

Now it is clear that, if formulae are to be simultaneously satisfiable, they must be satisfiable individually. But this is not the only condition. For '$(x)\,(fx)$' and '$(x)\,(\sim fx)$' are satisfiable individually but they are not simultaneously satisfiable. Obviously, if '$(x)\,(fx)$' is true, then 'fa' is true whatever we suppose 'a' to refer to. And similarly, if '$(x)\,(\sim fx)$' is true, then '$\sim fa$' is true, whatever be the referent of 'a'. But if 'fa' is true, then '$\sim fa$' must be false since '$(fa.\sim fa)$' is a contradictory truth-function. On the other hand, '$(x)\,(fx)$' and '$(x)\,(fx \supset gx)$' are simultaneously satisfiable. And this is shown by the fact that '$fa.(fa \supset ga)$' is *not* contradictory. This may be tested by constructing a truth-table:

$$fa \quad . \quad (fa \supset ga)$$

1	1	1	1	1
1	0	1	0	0
0	0	0	1	1
0	0	0	1	0

If the expression were *contradictory*, the second column (under the conjunction sign) would consist entirely of 0's. (The reader should construct for contrast the table for '$fa . \sim fa$'.)

Consequently we have the rule:

I. '(x) A' *and* '(x) B' *are simultaneously satisfiable if and only if* '$A.B$' *is truth-functionally consistent.**

Similar reasoning gives us:

II. '(x) A' *and* '$(\exists x)$ B' *are simultaneously satisfiable if and only if* '$A.B$' *is truth-functionally consistent.**

When we turn to case (iii) above, we have to formulate a different rule. '$(\exists x)(fx)$' and '$(\exists x)(\sim fx)$' are simultaneously satisfiable because '$(\exists x)(fx)$' is true if and only if

(1) $(fa_1 \vee fa_2 \vee \ldots \vee fa_n)$

is true, and '$(\exists x)(\sim fx)$' is true if and only if

(2) $(\sim fa_1 \vee \sim fa_2 \vee \ldots \vee \sim fa_n)$

is true.

Now (1) would be true if only *one* of the 'fa_1' to 'fa_n' were true. Suppose then that 'fa_1' is true and the rest *false*. Then '$\sim fa_2$' would be true and therefore (2) would be true, since (2) like (1) is true if *at least one* of the components of the disjunction is true. Thus (1) and (2) are clearly satisfiable simultaneously, and therefore

'$(\exists x)(fx)$' and '$(\exists x)(\sim fx)$'

are so as well. We therefore have:

III. '$(\exists x)$ A' *and* '$(\exists x)$ B' *are simultaneously satisfiable if and only if they are individually satisfiable.*

12. The Classical Syllogism. The following three formulae are not simultaneously satisfiable:

(1) $(x)(fx \supset gx)$, $(x)(gx \supset hx)$, $(\exists x)(fx . \sim hx)$.

---

* The rules are written thus for conciseness though strictly we should add: "*when the individual variables are replaced by individual constants distinct from any already appearing in* 'A' *and* 'B'". See page 117.

Applying the test developed in Section 11, we know that (1) will be simultaneously satisfiable only if:

(2) $(fa \supset ga).(ga \supset ha).(fa. \sim ha)$

is *consistent* by truth-tables, that is, if the main column of the truth-table contains *at least one* 1.   It is easy, however, to see that (2) is truth-functionally contradictory, that is, its truth-table contains only 0's in its main column.

The same result can be obtained intuitively by considering an interpretation of (1). Suppose '*f*' means "centaur", '*g*' means "vindictive", and '*h*' means "bold". Then:

(3) $(x) (fx \supset gx)$ means (3a) "All centaurs are vindictive".

(4) $(x) (gx \supset hx)$ means (4a) "All vindictive creatures are bold".

(5) $(\exists x) (fx. \sim hx)$ means (5a) "Some centaurs are not bold".

Clearly, if (3a) and (4a) are true, then (5a) must be false.

The set of formulae (1) is called *Ladd-Franklin's inconsistent triad** and it is the formal basis which validates most of the classical syllogisms. Since the three formulae are *not* simultaneously satisfiable, it is clear that given the truth of any two of them, we can infer the falsity of the third. Or given any two as premisses, we can infer the *negation* of the third. Thus:

(6) $((x) (fx \supset gx).(x) (gx \supset hx))$.
    Therefore $(x) (fx \supset hx)$;

(7) $((x) (fx \supset gx).(\exists x) (fx. \sim hx))$.
    Therefore $(\exists x) (gx. \sim hx)$;

(8) $((x) (gx \supset hx).(\exists x) (fx. \sim hx))$.
    Therefore $(\exists x) (fx. \sim gx)$;

are all valid forms of inference.

---

* After Mrs Christine Ladd-Franklin (1847-1930), an American logician.

The inferences mentioned in Section 1 all fall under one of the forms (6) to (8). Thus in Example (1) we may put 'f' for "ordinary members of the society", 'g' for "pay an annual subscription of one guinea", and 'h' for "receive the publications of the society without further charge". In Example (2) we put 'f' for "missionaries", 'g' for "has rigid views on morals", and 'h' for "does not make a good anthropologist". In (3) we put 'f' for "undergraduates", 'g' for "have the right to use the university library", and 'h' for "seriously interested in scholarship".

There are a few syllogisms which are not covered by the Ladd-Franklin formula. These are syllogisms in which a particular conclusion is drawn from universal premisses. For example:

All centaurs are vindictive.

All centaurs are bold.

Therefore, some vindictive creatures are bold.

Putting 'f' for "centaurs", 'g' for "vindictive", and 'h' for "bold", we get:

(9) $((x)(fx \supset gx).(x)(fx \supset hx))$. *Therefore* $(\exists x)(gx.hx)$.

By negating the conclusion of (9) we get the triad:

(10) $(x)(fx \supset gx)$, $(x)(fx \supset hx)$, $(x)(gx \supset \sim hx)$.

This is not the same as (1) and, moreover, it is consistent, for:

(11) $(fa \supset ga).(fa \supset ha).(ga \supset \sim ha)$

is true if we assign a meaning to 'a' such that 'fa', 'ga', and 'ha' are all false. This means that the inference is invalid if (and only if) there are no centaurs. Consequently, in order to render it valid, we must introduce an additional premiss asserting the existence of centaurs, getting [in place of (9)]:

(12) $((\exists x)\,(fx)\,.\,(x)\,(fx \supset gx)\,.\,(x)\,(fx \supset hx))$.

  Therefore $(\exists x)\,(gx\,.\,hx)$;

and [in place of (10)]

(13) $(\exists x)\,(fx),\,(x)\,(fx \supset gx),\,(x)\,(fx \supset hx),\,(x)\,(gx \supset \sim hx)$.

The four formulae (13) are not simultaneously satisfiable, since the truth-functional expression:

(14) $fa\,.\,(fa \supset ga)\,.\,(fa \supset ha)\,.\,(ga \supset \sim ha)$

is contradictory,* unlike (11).   Consequently the inference (12) is a valid one.   By taking any three of the four formulae in (13) as premisses, we can generate various forms of inference including some not recognised in the traditional scheme.

(A fuller treatment of the traditional approach to syllogistic inference is given in the Appendix.)

BIBLIOGRAPHICAL NOTE

CHAPTER V

Elementary accounts of the restricted predicate calculus fall into two classes, the descriptive and the more rigorous.   Good descriptive accounts will be found in Ambrose and Lazerowitz (1) and Strawson (30).   More rigorous elementary accounts are given in Cooley (7) and Reichenbach (25).   Eaton (10) gives a useful descriptive introduction to the symbolism of *Principia Mathematica* (33).   The most thorough treatment will be found in Hilbert and Ackermann (12).

* The student should check this for himself by constructing the appropriate truth-table.

CHAPTER VI

FURTHER DEVELOPMENTS

1. Extensions of the Class of Formulae. In Chapter V, we have considered in detail only a rather restricted class of formulae of the Predicate (or Functional) Calculus. Let us first state precisely the contents of this class:

(i) **Atomic formulae,** consisting of a single predicate constant followed by an individual variable. For example, 'fx', 'gx', 'fy', and the like.

(ii) **Truth functions of atomic formulae,** *all of which contain the same individual variable.* For example, '$fx \supset gx$', '$gy \lor hy$', and so on.

(iii) **Closed formulae,** which are the result of putting '$(\exists x)$' or '(x)', '$(\exists y)$', '(y)', and the like in front of formulae of types (i) and (ii). For example, '$(\exists x)(fx)$', '$(y)(gy \lor hy)$', and similar expressions. The variable occurring in the quantifier must here be the same as the variable occurring in the succeeding formula.

(iv) Truth functions of formulae of type (iii).

We consider especially the question of the *satisfiability* of these formulae and the simultaneous satisfiability of two or more of them taken together.

The restriction in (ii) will probably strike the reader as somewhat arbitrary. Why should we not allow formulae like '$fx \supset gy$' or even '$fx \supset fy$'? What would be the consequence of allowing such expressions? Let us investigate this possibility.

Consider the formula:

(1) $fx \supset gy$.

Since it is an open formula, it cannot be said to be true or false. We therefore apply the quantifier '$(\exists x)$', getting:

(2) $(\exists x)\,(fx \supset gy)$.

But this formula contains a free variable 'y', so we shall have to apply another quantifier, as for instance '$(\exists y)$'; we then have:

(3) $(\exists y)\,(\exists x)\,(fx \supset gy)$.

Now what meaning can we assign to (3)? We have some choice here but the most obvious meaning is:

(4) There is something x, and there is something y (*which may or may not be the same thing*), such that if x has the property f, then y has the property g.

Notice that this is quite different from the meaning of:

(5) $(\exists x)\,(fx \supset gx)$.

(5) says only that there is at least one object which *either* does not have the property 'f' or does have the property 'g'. (This proposition is so rarely false and so trivial as hardly ever to be worth asserting.)

A clearer example is perhaps the difference between:

(6) $(\exists y)\,(\exists x)\,(fx\,.\,gy)$ and

(7) $(\exists x)\,(fx\,.\,gx)$.

(6) says, under suitable interpretation, that, for example, there exists something red and something round, whereas (7) says under the same interpretation, that there exists something which is *both* red *and* round. And this is obviously quite a different matter.

Evidently we can construct formulae with triple and quadruple quantifiers on this model. Two questions then arise:

(*a*) What are the relations between these new formulae and the old ones?

and, in particular,

(*b*) Do these new formulae constitute a genuine extension of our calculus?

We shall proceed first to say something about these two questions.

2. Formulae with more than one Quantifier. Let us consider the second question first. We must first express it more exactly:

(*b′*) Do some or all of the new formulae have meanings which cannot be expressed by means of the old formulae?

For this purpose, we shall say that two formulae, '*P*' and '*Q*', *have the same meaning* if whatever interpretation satisfies '*P*' satisfies '*Q*', and conversely. The answer to question (*b′*) is in fact: No. The new formulae do not constitute a genuine extension over the old ones. We cannot give a formal proof of this here but a few examples will make clear the relationship between the new formulae and the old. Consider the formulae:

(1) $(\exists x).(\exists y)\,(fx.gy)$.

(2) $(\exists x)\,(fx).(\exists x)\,(gx)$.

(3) $(\exists x)\,(fx.gx)$.

A little reflection will convince the reader that, although (1) and (3) do not have the same meaning, (1) and (2) *do* have the same meaning. Likewise,

(4) $(\exists x)\,(\exists y)\,(fx \vee gy)$

means the same as:

(5) $(\exists x)\,(fx) \vee (\exists x)\,(gx)$.

For in (4) the bound variables '*x*' and '*y*' may or may not refer to the same individuals. And the same is true of the two occurrences of '*x*' in the quantifiers of (5).

Consequently, since '$P \supset Q$' is the same as '$\sim P \vee Q$',

(6) $(\exists x)(\exists y)(fx \supset gy)$

is the same as:

(7) $(\exists x)(\exists y)(\sim fx \vee gy)$

which, in turn, is the same as:

(8) $(\exists x)(\sim fx) \vee (\exists y)(gy)$.

Thus these formulae with two quantified variables may be resolved into truth-functional combinations of formulae with only one variable quantified. These facts suggest (but do not, of course, *prove*) what actually is the case, namely, that formulae with several quantifications can always be transformed into equivalent formulae which are truth-functions of formulae with single quantifications. Because of this fact, the introduction of such formulae is of little theoretical interest and we shall not discuss it further here. The extension is, of course, of considerable *practical* interest inasmuch as it enables us to formalise arguments of greater complexity. But the method of deciding the validity of such arguments is no different from that already discussed in Chapter V.*

3. Two-termed Predicates. An extension of much greater theoretical interest is the introduction of *two-termed predicates* into our system. Certain singular propositions contain two or more proper names. For example:

(1) John is taller than James.

(2) Reading is between Oxford and London.

---

* In view of the discussion in Section 3 below, it will be well to emphasise that what we have been saying here relates only to expressions containing one-term predicates (or one-place predicates) like "blue" or "hot". It is not applicable to expressions containing the more complex predicates introduced in Section 3.

These propositions assert the existence of a *relation* between two or more individual objects. They could be expressed symbolically by:

(3) *fab*.

(4) *fabc*.

In (3) the letter '*f*' can be interpreted to mean the relation of "being taller than"; and in (4) the letter '*f*' can be interpreted as "being between". "Taller than" is said to be a two-termed or *dyadic* relation; and "between" is three-termed or *triadic*. And it is possible to think of *tetradic* relations or of relations of even higher orders but mention of these relations does not often occur in ordinary discourse.

Using variables and quantifiers, we can obtain formulae like:

(5) $(\exists x)\,(\exists y)\,(fxy)$.

(6) $(\exists x)\,(y)\,(fxy)$.

If '*f*' is interpreted to mean "taller than", then (5) expresses the true proposition:

(7) There exists an x and a y such that x is taller than y.

And (6) expresses, under the same interpretation, the false proposition:

(8) There is an x such that, for all values of y, x is taller than y.

This is false because no object can be taller than itself. The introduction of dyadic and other relations into logic marks an advance of the greatest importance. It may perhaps appear at first sight that they are just ordinary predicates like "blue" or "hot" or any other predicate of the type dealt with in the previous chapter, the only difference between them being that "blue" is a one-place predicate qualifying only one thing at each of its occurrences, whereas "between", for example, is a three-place predicate requiring three individuals to qualify each time it is instantiated. This is correct; but the important point is that the transition from one-place predicates to predicates of two or more places introduces considerable complexities into logic.

We have seen that the essential problem in the logic of predicates is the problem of the *satisfiability* of some given class of quantified formulae. Up to the present, we have treated this question of satisfiability in an *intuitive* way; that is to say, we have contented ourselves with the fact that a formula is satisfiable if we can assign meanings to the predicate terms in it so that by our interpretation we obtain a true proposition. We then developed a technique, applicable to a restricted class of formulae, namely, those formulae which we discussed in Chapter V, which would enable us to say whether or not a particular formula is satisfiable and whether or not a particular finite set of formulae are simultaneously satisfiable.

For reasons which will become clear later, we cannot extend this intuitive approach to formulae that contain two-termed predicates. It is essential that we should now undertake a careful analysis of the notion of satisfiability and give a *precise* and *rigorous* definition of what we propose to mean by saying that a formula is satisfiable. This analytic approach will not invalidate anything which we have said so far. But it will issue in a deeper understanding of the notion of satisfiability which is, indeed, a keystone of logic.

4. Satisfiability: Finite Domains. Suppose that we have a little group of, say, three different objects; and suppose we confine our attention to this little group and always interpret our formulae in terms of these objects, their properties and their relations. We call the objects A, B, and C. Such a set of objects, used for the purposes of interpreting formulae, is called a *domain* or *universe of discourse*.*

Now consider a predicate of ordinary discourse like "red". This predicate will divide our three objects into two classes, according as they are or are not red. In this sense, "red" *defines a class* in the domain ABC, namely, the class of red objects in the domain.

Now consider the various possible classes in the domain ABC. There are exactly eight, namely:

(*a*) The null class† (the class consisting of no objects at all).

(*b*) The three classes whose only members are A, B, and C respectively.

(*c*) The three classes whose only members are A and B, A and C, B and C respectively.

(*d*) The class containing A, B, and C, that is the class co-extensive with the domain.

These classes can be written as follows: (1) [0], (2) [A], (3) [B], (4) [C], (5) [AB], (6) [AC], (7) [BC], (8) [ABC].‡ Now it is clear that, no matter what predicates we use to define a class in this domain, it must always define one or other of these eight classes. Moreover, a large number of different predicates will define the *same* class, and in ordinary language these different predicates would nonetheless have different meanings. For example, A may be the only red object in the domain *and also* the only round object. Thus, "red" and "round" define the same class in this domain. Nevertheless, "red" and "round" have quite different meanings.

---

* For a further discussion of this concept, see Appendix.

† For a more general discussion of this concept and of the notion of class, see Appendix.

‡ Notice the use of square brackets here; [AC] means "the class whose only members are A and C", and so on.

Suppose we are given some formula involving one-termed predicates, for example, '$(\exists x)(fx)$', and try to interpret it in the domain ABC. In a sense, we can give any number of different meanings to 'f', but these meanings will all define one or other of the eight classes mentioned. Consequently, so far as satisfiability in this domain is concerned, *only eight effectively different* interpretations of 'f' can be given.

We can now see that the question of the satisfiability of any formula (containing only one-term predicates) *in the domain ABC* is easy to determine. There is no need to hunt through innumerable different meanings for the various predicate terms. All we need to consider are the eight effectively different meanings, namely, the eight different possible assignments of a given predicate to the classes in the domain ABC. For example, '$(\exists x)(fx.\sim gx)$' is satisfiable in this domain, because if 'f' is associated with [A] and 'g' with [B],* there will be something, namely A, which has the property 'f' and not the property 'g'.

5. Finite Domains (*continued*). We took as our example a domain containing just three objects and explained what is meant by saying that a formula is satisfiable in such a domain. But it is clear that we could have considered a domain containing one or two or twenty-six or any other finite number of objects. (Later we shall see that even *infinite* domains play their part.) And we can even conceive of an empty domain containing no objects whatever.

Two questions then arise: (*a*) Are there formulae which are satisfiable in some domains but not in others? (*b*) Are there formulae which are *not* satisfiable in *any* domain? To answer these questions we have first to state explicitly what we mean by "different domains". Let us first do this.

* We say that 'f' is associated with [A], the class whose only member is A, if we have assigned a meaning, *e.g.* "red" to 'f', such that A is the only object in the domain with this property.

Definition 1.—By different domains, we shall mean domains containing different *numbers* of objects. In other words, domains containing the same number of objects are identical for logical purposes, no matter whether the objects in the domains are different or not.

This definition underlies what is meant by saying that logic is a matter of *form* and not of subject-matter or *content*. (See Chapter I.)

Question (*a*) can be answered easily enough. The formula '$(\exists x)(fx)$' is not satisfiable in the empty domain. Indeed, no existential proposition can be satisfied in the empty domain, for obvious reasons. Again, '$(\exists x)(\exists y)(fx . \sim fy)$' is not satisfiable in a domain which contains *less than two* distinct objects. In general, we have:

(1) For any finite number n, there are formulae which are not satisfiable in any domain containing less than n objects.

(2) If a formula is satisfiable in a domain containing n objects, then it will be satisfiable in every domain containing more than n objects.

These facts suggest the following definition of "satisfiability in general":

Definition 2.—A formula is satisfiable (in general) if and only if there exists a finite domain in which it is satisfiable.

Likewise:

Definition 3.—Two or more formulae are simultaneously satisfiable (or *consistent*) if and only if there exists a finite domain in which they are simultaneously satisfiable.

The reader will perhaps have noticed that these definitions, taken as they stand, are *not completely rigorous*. This is because, although we have assigned a meaning to the phrase "not satisfiable in an empty domain", we have not defined what we mean by saying that a formula *is* satisfiable in the empty domain. We can give this phrase a meaning but we shall, in fact, avoid this issue altogether by amending definitions (2) and (3) as follows:

Definition 2a.—A formula is satisfiable (in general) if and only if there exists a finite *non-empty* domain in which it is satisfiable.

Definition 3a.—Two or more formulae are simultaneously satisfiable (or *consistent*) if and only if there exists a finite *non-empty* domain in which they are simultaneously satisfiable.

6. Two-termed Predicates: Infinite Domains. The definitions that we have given for satisfiability and consistency work quite well for formulae containing one-term predicates only, that is, for all the formulae discussed in Chapter V. Indeed, our decision method there is based on an intuitive use of just the notions which we have now more rigorously expressed. The question now arises: Are these definitions adequate also for formulae containing two-termed predicates, for example '$(x)\,(fxy)$' and the like? The answer to this is that they are *not* adequate. And the fact that they are not adequate is one of the most important facts of logic.

First consider the formula:

(1) $(x)\,(y)\,(fxy \supset \sim fyx)$.

This formula is satisfiable intuitively. For suppose 'f' to mean "greater than". Then (1) will mean:

(2) Whatever x and y may be, if x is greater than y, then y is not greater than x.

Clearly (1) is satisfiable in a finite domain, for example, the domain containing only the integers 1 and 2. [Of course, a multitude of other meanings besides "greater than" will satisfy (1). For example, "father of", "to the left of", "later than".]

Now consider:

(3) $(x) (y) (z) (fxy) \supset (fyz \supset fxz)$.

(3) is satisfied by "equal to", "greater than", but not by "greater by one than".

(4) $(y) (\exists x) (fxy)$.

(4) is satisfied by "equal to".

Now let us ask ourselves if (1), (3), and (4) are *consistent*, that is, simultaneously satisfiable. Clearly, the validity of many forms of inference depends on the answer to this question.

Suppose D_n is a domain of n objects, $a_1, a_2, \ldots a_n$, and R is a relation which satisfies (1), that is, if a_m has the relation R to a_n, then it is *not* the case that a_n has the relation R to a_m. We may write this:

if $(a_m R a_n)$, then not-$(a_n R a_m)$.

Suppose that R also satisfies (3), that is:

if $(a_m R a_n)$ and $(a_n R a_j)$, then $(a_m R a_j)$,

and, consequently, it is not the case that $(a_j R a_m)$. Now choose any object in the domain, say, a_1. If (4) is to be satisfied, there must be some object, say, a_2, such that $(a_1 R a_2)$ and similarly $(a_2 R a_3)$ and so on. We can then form a *chain*:

$(a_1 R a_2) . (a_2 R a_3) . (a_3 R a_4) . \ldots . (a_{k-1} R a_k)$.

Any such chain must terminate since it cannot contain more than the n objects in the domain. But by (3), if a_j precedes a_k in the chain, then it is not the case that $(a_k R a_j)$. Hence there must be some object in the domain which contradicts (4).

Nevertheless, the three formulae are clearly satisfiable in an intuitive sense. For let the domain be the domain of positive integers and let 'f' mean "greater than"; then (1) and (3) are satisfied and (4) is also satisfied, since for any number k, there is a number m such that m is greater than k. This is so because the sequence of positive integers *does not terminate*, which is to say that it is an *infinite domain*.

We saw in Section 4 that some finite domains may be bigger than (*i.e.* contain more objects than) others and that this is the difference between domains which is important for logic. We agreed to say that two domains are *abstractly* or *logically identical* if they contain the same number of objects. A question naturally arises: Are some *infinite* domains in some sense bigger than others or are all infinite domains abstractly identical? In other words, are there for the purposes of logic one or many abstractly distinct infinite domains? A complete answer to this question does not come within the scope of this book. For our present purpose, we shall assume for simplicity that there is only one infinite domain. This is not in fact the case but for the limited purposes of the present discussion it will be less confusing if we talk simply of "the infinite domain". The following rules are not invalidated by the fact that this assumption is incorrect. We can now, therefore, set out some rules for satisfiability as follows:

Rule 1.—If a formula is satisfiable in some finite domain, then it is satisfiable in the infinite domain.

Rule 2.—If a formula *containing one-term predicates only* is satisfiable at all, then it is satisfiable in some *finite* domain.

Rule 3.—There exist formulae containing *two-term* predicates which are satisfiable *only* in the infinite domain.

7. Logical Truth. In Chapter II we divided the formulae of the propositional calculus into two classes, tautologies and those formulae which are not tautologies. A tautology is said to be a *logically true* formula in this sense that it guarantees a certain form of inference. A question arises: Can we specify a similar class of formulae for the predicate calculus? We can do this by making use of the notion of satisfiability.

We explained in the two previous sections what was meant by saying that a formula is satisfiable in a domain D_n containing a definite number n of objects. We can therefore divide our formulae into two classes:

(A) Formulae which are satisfiable in D_n.

(B) Formulae which are not satisfiable in D_n.

Now let us consider the following class:

(C) Formulae whose negations are members of (B).

(C) will be said to form the class of formulae which are *valid in D_n*. It is clear that no matter what interpretation we give to such formulae (within the limits of D_n), they will always express true propositions.

If we are assumed to know beforehand the number of objects in our domain, the formulae valid in that domain will guarantee various forms of inference in just the same way as tautologies. If, however, as is usually the case, the number of objects in the domain is unknown to us, then clearly, the assumption that the domain contains any particular number of objects may lead to fallacious inferences. For this reason, we cannot be content with formulae which are valid in some domains and not in others. We require our formulae to be valid *in every domain* with perhaps a certain exception.

The exception is that we need not require our formulae to be valid in the *empty* domain. This is just a matter of convenience. For example, we are permitted, if we make this exception, to treat such a formula as '$(\exists x)\,(fx \lor \sim fx)$'

as valid. It would be most inconvenient if, in our inferences, we were constantly obliged to insert an explicit premiss to the effect that something exists in the universe of discourse. It is much more convenient to take the matter for granted.

The reader may wonder if we now possess a complete specification of logical truth. Could we perhaps extend the class of formulae in some way and then construct for this extended class of formulae some standard of logical truth which is stronger than the notion of validity discussed above in the way that this notion is stronger than the notion of tautology? The answer to this question is fraught with great difficulties and we cannot discuss it in any detail here. We can indeed extend our class of formulae, getting the so-called *Extended Predicate Calculus*. But this calculus is not more powerful than our *Restricted Predicate Calculus* in the way that the latter is more powerful than the Propositional Calculus.

8. Decision Procedures. By a *decision procedure*, we understand some method of deciding *whether or not* any arbitrarily given formula of a certain class is logically true. We have such procedures for the formulae of the Propositional Calculus, namely, the method of truth-tables or the method of conjunctive normal forms. The features of these methods which make them decision procedures are:

(i) They are applicable to *any* formula of the Propositional Calculus.

(ii) They always arrive at an answer (either that the formula is a tautology or that it is not a tautology) after a limited amount of calculation.

We also have a decision procedure for the *calculus of one-termed predicates*. In Chapter V we explained a method of deciding whether or not any given formula of a certain kind is satisfiable. And we have seen that a formula is valid if and only if its negation is *unsatisfiable*. Here, however, our decision procedure rests on two assumptions:

(1) That any formula '*A*' of the whole calculus of one-termed predicates can be associated with some formula '*B*' of the restricted class of Chapter V such that '*A*' is valid if and only if '*B*' is valid.

(2) If a formula of the calculus of one-termed predicates is valid in every (non-empty) finite domain, it is also valid in the infinite domain.

As it happens, both these assumptions are true but the reader should appreciate that we have not in fact verified them. (Their proofs lie beyond the scope of this book.) Consequently, our proof that there is such a procedure remains incomplete.

If we add to our formulae those containing two-, three-, or, in general, *n*-termed predicates, we get the so-called Restricted Predicate Calculus. Have we a decision procedure for this calculus? The answer is that we do not have such a procedure and, moreover, are never likely to have. The reason for this is not easy to explain without going into considerable technical detail. It is, however, closely associated with the fact that assumption (2) above does not hold for the Restricted Predicate Calculus as a whole. A few general remarks may help the reader.

A decision procedure is essentially a *mechanical* process. If we can give such a procedure, we can always devise, in theory at least, a machine which will carry it out without human intervention. Now the most general concept of such a calculating machine which is known to us was put forward by Dr A. M. Turing in 1936. All machines which fall under this concept are called Turing machines. What we know for certain is that *if* a decision procedure for the Restricted Predicate Calculus is ever devised, then the corresponding machine will *not* be a Turing machine. We really have not the smallest concept of what a calculating machine would be like if it was not a Turing machine nor have we even the faintest idea of how such a machine would work.

9. Axiom Systems. By an *axiom system* we mean a method for deriving logically true formulae. Such a system usually consists of:

(1) A finite number of axioms.

(2) A finite number of rules of inference.

We have given one example of an axiom system, namely, a system for deriving all the logically true formulae of the Propositional Calculus. It is clear that ideally the following two conditions must be satisfied:

(i) Every logically true formula (of the desired class) must be derivable.

(ii) No formula that is not logically true can be derivable.

We proved that our axiom system for the Propositional Calculus met these two conditions.

We may naturally ask: Can such a complete and consistent axiom system be devised for the Restricted Predicate Calculus? The answer is that an axiom system for this purpose can be devised without great difficulty. In fact, axiom systems for the Restricted Predicate Calculus are sometimes given, though without the required proofs of completeness and consistency, in elementary books. We have not given one here only because the considerations leading to its construction and to the proofs of its consistency and completeness, while not especially difficult, do require a perfect understanding of the basic notions of validity and satisfiability. Once he is sure of these, the reader is in a position to consult the necessary sources. (See the bibliographical note at the end of the chapter.)

Axiom systems are closely related to decision procedures. In fact, a complete and consistent axiom system is one-half of a decision procedure, for if a formula is logically true, it can tell us that this is the case. It is obvious, however, that if a formula is *not* logically true (and therefore not in the list of derivable formulae) no extension of this list will inform us of the fact. In view of the close relation between axiom systems and decision procedures, it is somewhat surprising that the first is possible for the Restricted Predicate Calculus, while the second, it seems, is not. What it amounts to is that we have a way of listing all the valid formulae but no way of listing all the invalid ones. No matter what method we choose for making a list of all the invalid formulae of this calculus, either it leaves out some or it will include in the list some which are valid.

BIBLIOGRAPHICAL NOTE

CHAPTER VI

The best elementary discussions of some of the problems raised in this chapter will be found in Quine (24). Reichenbach (25) gives an excellent account of the techniques of the predicate calculus. The standard text is again Hilbert and Ackermann (12). For a discussion of Turing machines, see Kleene (18).

GENERAL

Kleene (18) is a very thorough and rigorous survey of the field of symbolic logic in its relation to mathematics. It is not an easy book and the student should not attempt it until he has mastered Hilbert and Ackermann (12). Good general works on symbolic logic beyond the merely elementary level are Copi (34), Fitch (11), Leblanc (35), Lewis and Langford (20), Quine (23), and Reichenbach (25). Strawson (30) has an excellent discussion of the relation between logic and ordinary language. Rosenbloom (26) is a concise and systematic survey which will be useful to the student with some knowledge and appreciation of mathematical techniques. The best elementary book is Ambrose and Lazerowitz (1). Students who read French will find J. Dopp: *Lecons de Logique Formelle*, a first class introduction.

APPENDIX

1. The Syllogism and the Algebra of Classes. The theory of the syllogism comprises almost the whole of the deductive logic of the traditional textbooks. It would not therefore be proper, even in so brief an outline of modern logic, to pass the syllogism by with only the cursory reference already given.* It is true that the types of argument embodied in the various forms of the syllogism can be adequately dealt with by the symbolism and procedures of the restricted predicate calculus which have been outlined in Chapters V and VI. Thus, the parts of logic which have been discussed in this book include the logic of the syllogism. But the theory of the syllogism can be conveniently related to another important branch of logic, the algebra of classes, which has so far received only a passing reference in Chapter I.

The following brief account of the "Aristotelian" syllogism is put in here for the sake of completeness and for the benefit of those readers who are quite unacquainted with the traditional logic. More detailed accounts will be found in the books quoted at the end of the chapter. It may be as well to mention, however, that the word "Aristotelian", though usual in this context, is misleading. Aristotle was, of course, the inventor of the syllogism but his own treatment of it differs in several important particulars from those given in the traditional textbooks. (An authoritative account of these differences has recently been given by Professor Lukasiewicz.)†

We shall understand by the term "syllogism" what the textbooks of the traditional logic refer to as the *categorical*

---

* Section 12 of Chapter V.
† *Aristotle's Syllogistic* (Oxford, 1951).

syllogism. (The so-called *hypothetical* and *disjunctive* syllogisms are really truth-functional arguments which can be dealt with by the methods of Chapters II and III.) The following are instances of syllogisms:

(1) All finches are grain eaters.
   Some finches are migrants.
   Therefore, some migrants are grain eaters.

(2) No acts of injustice are politically expedient.
   Some emergency measures are acts of injustice.
   Therefore, some emergency measures are not politically expedient.

The reader will see that each of the examples given (like the examples quoted at the beginning of Chapter V) consist of three propositions, two *premisses* followed by a *conclusion* which is stated as the logical consequence of the conjunction of the two premisses. If we represent the premisses by 'P_1' and 'P_2' and the conclusion by 'C', the form of the argument is:

(3) $(P_1.P_2) \supset C$.

But this symbolism, as we have seen already, does not make the logical point of the argument clear. (3) is not a valid formula. The validity of arguments like (1) and (2) rests on certain relations between the *classes* referred to in the premisses and these relations are not brought out by (3). In (2), for example, the classes are "acts of injustice", "politically expedient acts", and "emergency measures".

In the traditional syllogism, the terms standing for the classes were given special names. The term occurring twice in the premisses is called the *middle term*; the terms which are subject and predicate of the conclusion are known respectively as the *minor term* and the *major term*. Thus, in (1), the middle term is "finches" and the minor and major terms are "migrants" and "grain eaters" respectively.

In accordance with this terminology, the premiss containing the minor term is known as the minor premiss and that containing the major term is called the major premiss. And it is conventional, though in no way relevant to the *validity* of the argument, to put the major premiss before the minor in setting out a syllogism.

Further, the propositions used in an Aristotelian syllogism are classified into four different kinds. Those propositions like the major premisses of (1) and (2) above which say something (positive or negative) about the *whole* of the subject class are called *universal* propositions. Those propositions, like the minor premiss and conclusions of (1) and (2) which make an assertion about *a part only* of the subject class are known as *particular* propositions. Moreover, propositions may be classified further as *affirmative* or *negative* according as they affirm or deny the predicate of the subject. For example, the major premiss of (2) and its conclusion are negative, while the minor premiss is affirmative. We thus have four types of proposition (and only four) forming the basic units of classical logic. They have been distinguished for convenience, since early medieval times, by letters assigned to them as follows:

> universal affirmative: A
>
> universal negative: E
>
> particular affirmative: I
>
> particular negative: O

A term in an Aristotelian syllogism is said to be *distributed* if the proposition in which it occurs refers to the *whole* of the class designated by the term. Otherwise, the term is *undistributed*. Consider the following propositons:

(4) All athletes are energetic (A).

(5) No burglars are respecters of property rights (E).

(6) Some film stars are glamorous (I).

(7) Some snakes are not poisonous (O).

It is clear that the universal propositions (A and E) distribute their *subject* terms. If I say "All athletes are energetic", I identify *every* member of the class of athletes with some member of the class of energetic people. If I say "no burglars are respecters of property rights", I exclude *every* burglar from the class of respecters of property rights. On the other hand, all particular propositions (I and O) have their subject terms *undistributed*. This is clear because such propositions are of the form "Some S is P" or "Some S is not P". We do not refer to *all* the members of the class S.

All negative propositions, both universal (E) and particular (O) distribute their *predicate* terms. In asserting (5), I not only exclude all burglars from the class of those who respect property rights but I also exclude *all the members of the predicate class*, "respecters of property rights", from the class of burglars. Similarly, in asserting (7), although I make an assertion about only *part* of the class of snakes I exclude this class from the *whole* of the predicate class "poisonous things".

We may summarise the position by saying that all universal propositions distribute their subject terms and all negative propositions distribute their predicate terms. Thus we have:

A (universal affirmative) distributes subject only.

I (particular affirmative) distributes neither subject nor predicate.

E (universal negative) distributes both subject and predicate.

O (particular negative) distributes the predicate only.

We are now in a position to state the rules which govern the validity of the syllogism. They are as follows:

(i) The middle term must be distributed at least once.

(ii) No term may be distributed in the conclusion which was not distributed in its premiss.

(iii) No conclusion follows from two negative premisses.

(iv) (a) If one premiss is negative, the conclusion must be negative.

(b) If the conclusion is negative, one premiss must be negative.

These rules are usually treated as *axioms* of syllogistic logic and a number of corollaries may be derived from them. (For example, no conclusion follows from two particular premisses.) They are not, however, *independent* axioms and some of them can be shown to be consequences of the others.*

Let us now consider the question: How many different types of valid syllogism are there? It is obvious that the number of *possibilities* is considerable. In any syllogism, there are four different types of proposition available as major premiss (A, E, I, and O). Similarly, there are four different possibilities for the minor premiss and the same number for the conclusion. Thus, considering only the types of propositions involved, there are (4 × 4 × 4) or sixty-four possible kinds of syllogism. [These different combinations of premisses and conclusion, for example, AII in (1) above or EIO in (2), are known as the *moods* of the syllogism.]

But we have also to consider the possible ways of arranging our major, minor, and middle terms. There are *four* possible arrangements. Representing the middle term by M, the major term by P, and the minor by S we have:

I		II		III		IV	
M	P	P	M	M	P	P	M
S	M	S	M	M	S	M	S
S	P	S	P	S	P	S	P

* Keynes: *Formal Logic* (Fourth Edition), pp. 291-4.

These four possible arrangements are known as the *figures* of the syllogism. It is clearly possible to express any of the sixty-four possible moods of the syllogism in any of the four figures, giving in all 256 possible different types of syllogism. Fortunately, however, if we apply the rules of the syllogism to these possibilities we find that only twenty-four of them are valid. Of these five are the so-called weakened moods in which a particular conclusion is drawn from premisses which justify a universal. (For example, AAI in Figure I instead of AAA.) Omitting these as unimportant, we have nineteen valid moods as follows:

Figure 1		*Figure II*	
AAA	(Barbara)	EAE	(Cesare)
EAE	(Celarent)	AEE	(Camestres)
AII	(Darii)	EIO	(Festino)
EIO	(Ferio)	AOO	(Baroco)

Figure III		*Figure IV*	
AAI	(Darapti)	AAI	(Bramantip)
IAI	(Disamis)	AEE	(Camenes)
AII	(Datisi)	IAI	(Dimaris)
EAO	(Felapton)	EAO	(Fesapo)
OAO	(Bocardo)	EIO	(Fresison)
EIO	(Ferison)		

The "proper names" of the individual moods, given in brackets, are convenient traditional ways of referring to the valid moods. Thus, "Darapti" means "AAI in Figure III", and so on. The names are taken from a Latin mnemonic verse, the earliest version of which is found in the works of a medieval logician, Peter of Spain, later Pope John XXI.

2. Classes and the Relationships between them. In the syllogism, as we have seen, we are concerned with *classes* of things. In (1) of the foregoing section, for example, the syllogism concerns the classes "finches", "grain eaters", and "migrants". The notion of class is one which is basic to logic and, indeed, familiar from common-sense discourse. We shall not, therefore, try to define it more exactly than by saying that a class is any set, collection, or aggregate whose members have some property in common. This property is the *defining property* of the class. (The reader will notice that this account of classes, which is based on the usage of the word "class" in everyday discourse, differs from that given in Chapter VI, Section 4. There we regarded classes *extensionally*, that is, from the point of view of the *members* of the class. Here we are taking the more usual course of regarding a class *intensionally*, that is, from the point of view of the *property common* to all the members of the class. It should be noticed that these two points of view are not inconsistent. Both are legitimate and it is a matter of convenience which one we adopt. Because we are here considering classes from the intensional point of view, we shall not adopt the same notation as that used in Chapter VI.)

In adopting this common-sense notion of class to logical use, we shall find it convenient to extend it a little. In ordinary language, a class is a group or collection of things that have some property in common. It would not, therefore, be usual to talk of a class with only *one* member and still less usual to talk of a class with no members at all. Yet these extensions of the meaning of the word "class" are convenient and, indeed, necessary in logic.

The class of kings of England who have had six wives has only one member, namely, Henry VIII. And the class of kings of England who have been executed has only one member, namely, Charles I. And it is important to notice that we cannot dispense with these *unit-classes*, as they are called, by identifying the class with its only member. For they are not identical. "Henry VIII died in 1547" is a true statement. But the statement "the class of kings of England who have had six wives died in 1547" is neither true nor even false: it is meaningless. We shall require, in addition to the concept of a unit-class, the concept of the *null class*, or the class that has no members. The following descriptive phrases may be said to characterise the null class in that they describe nothing at all: "being an even prime greater than two", "being a round square", "being a mermaid", "being the king of Germany in 1950". It is clear that instances of this kind may be multiplied indefinitely. It should be noticed, however, that though we can find an indefinitely large number of properties which characterise the null class, we do not assume that there is a separate null class corresponding to each of these properties. We need not postulate, for example, a null class of mermaids and *another* null class comprising the even primes greater than two because this would introduce unnecessary complications and redundancies. It can be assumed that there is only one null class. And it can be *proved* that no mistakes in logic follow from the thesis that there is only one. The very notion of such a class may seem at first sight to be artificial and unnecessary but it will be seen as we proceed that it is in fact essential for the systematic development of the calculus of classes.

The Complement Class and the Universe of Discourse.— We shall use italic capital letters from the beginning of the alphabet A, B, C, . . . to represent classes. Then A stands, let us say, for the class of dogs. To such a class we can obviously construct a *complementary* class, namely, the class of all those things which are not dogs. Let us represent this class by A'. Thus the *extension* of A is all the dogs in the universe and the extension of A' is all those things which are *not* dogs. The question now arises: what is to be included in A'? Things are diverse as cats, fish, buttercups, prime numbers, the British navy, and quadratic equations would qualify for membership, as, indeed, would anything in the universe that is not a dog. Now it is found that serious difficulties arise from admitting into logic such diverse and catholic membership of classes. We therefore restrict ourselves when we are talking of classes to a given *universe of discourse*. This concept was introduced into logic by De Morgan (1806-71). He explains it in the following way:* "Let us take a pair of contrary names, as man and not-man. It is plain that between them they represent everything imaginable or real in the universe. But the contraries† of common language usually embrace, not the whole universe, but some one general idea. Thus of men, Briton and alien are contraries: every man must be one of the two, no man can be both. Not-Briton and alien are identical names, and so are not-alien and Briton. The same may be said of integer and fraction among numbers, peer and commoner among subjects of the realm, male and female among animals, and so on. In order to express this, let us say that the whole idea under consideration is *the universe* (meaning merely the whole of which we are considering parts) and let names which have nothing in common, but which between them contain the whole idea under consideration, be called contraries *in, or with respect to, that universe*. Thus the universe being mankind, Briton and alien are contraries as are soldier and civilian, male and female, etc. The universe being animal, man and brute are contraries, etc."

* *Formal Logic* (edited Taylor), London, 1926, p. 42.
† Although De Morgan uses the word "contraries" here, it would now be more usual to speak, in this context, of *contradictories*.

We have therefore two classes, *A* and *A'*, which comprise between them the whole of a given universe of discourse. We may represent this universe and its constituent classes diagrammatically in the following way:

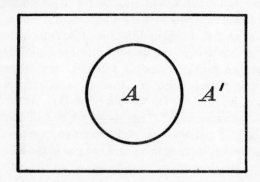

Thus the class of animals, if we take this as our universe of discourse, can be divided into two mutually exclusive and collectively exhaustive classes, dogs and not-dogs.

Basic Class Relationships.—One of the fundamental facts about classes is that, with the exception of the null class, they all have members. The relation of a member to the class of which it is a member is usually symbolised by the Greek letter 'ϵ'. Thus the form of sentences like:

    (1) Socrates is wise,

    (2) Tray is a dog,

    (3) Napoleon is dead,

can be symbolised, not only by using the symbolism of the predicate calculus as:

    (4) fx,

but also by:

    (5) $x\epsilon A$,

where 'x' is, as before, an individual variable and 'A' is a class variable. Thus we use 'ϵ' as a logical constant to represent the relation of class membership.

A further basic relation is that of class inclusion. The statement:

    (6) Socrates is mortal

is to be distinguished sharply, in virtue of its logical form, from:

    (7) All men are mortal.

(6) states that a given *individual* is a *member* of a certain class, while (7) states that a given *class* is *included in* another class. (6) is symbolised by (5). But to represent (7) in symbolic form, we must introduce another logical constant '$\subset$', and write (7) as:

    (8) $A \subset B$.

The fundamental difference between the relations symbolised by 'ϵ' and '$\subset$' may be brought out as follows: '$\subset$' represents a *transitive* relation, while 'ϵ' does not. A transitive relation is a relation R such that if x has R to y and y has R to z, then x has R to z. The relation "larger than" is an instance. If $x > y$ and $y > z$, then $x > z$. Obviously, "included in" is another instance. If $A \subset B$ and $B \subset C$, then $A \subset C$. But the relation of "class membership" is not transitive. If Jones is a member of the British nation and the British nation is a member of the United Nations Organisation, then it does *not* follow that Jones is a member of UNO. For only nations, not individuals, qualify as members of UNO.

Class Sum and Class Product.—Suppose that we take as our universe of discourse the class of human beings and select for attention two sub-classes, the class of blue-eyed people and the class of black-haired people. Then we have, within the universe of discourse which we have selected, four classes (and only four) which are mutually exclusive and also collectively exhaustive of the whole universe. They are:

   (a) blue-eyed people who are black haired,

   (b) blue-eyed people who are not black haired,

   (c) black-haired people who are not blue eyed,

   (d) people who are neither blue eyed nor black haired.

Let *A* be the class of blue-eyed persons and *B* the class of black-haired persons. We then have, symbolising (a) to (d) above:

   (a) AB,

   (b) AB',

   (c) $A'B$.

   (d) $A'B'$.

And we may represent our universe and its constituent classes on a Venn diagram* thus:

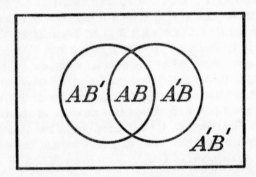

In this diagram, the overlap between the *A*-circle and the *B*-circle represents the class of people who are *both* blue eyed *and* black haired. This class is called the *logical*

* This form of diagram was introduced by the Cambridge logician, John Venn (1834-1923).

product or the intersection of the two classes. On the other hand, the two circles themselves represent the *logical sum* or *union* of the two classes and form a further class, namely, the class of people who are *either* blue eyed *or* black haired (or both).

Symbolism for the Class Calculus.—The concepts so far introduced will be symbolised thus:

(i)	classes	$A, B, C, \ldots$
(ii)	class complements	$A', B', C', \ldots$
(iii)	null class	0
(iv)	universe of discourse	1
(v)	class membership	ϵ
(vi)	class inclusion	$\subset$
(vii)	logical product of two classes	$A \times B$, or, for short, AB
(viii)	logical sum of two classes	$A + B$.

The reader will see that we may combine two or more classes to make a further class by means of the appropriate logical constants, just as in the propositional calculus we may combine two or more propositions to make a further proposition. Thus, to revert to the example taken above:

(9) $A'B + B'$

stands for the class of people who are *either* both black haired and not blue eyed *or* not black haired.

3. The Boolean Algebra of Classes. The development of the notions outlined above into a formal calculus of classes is largely the work of George Boole (1815-64). In a short book entitled *The Mathematical Analysis of Logic*, published in 1847, he outlined the system in a substantially complete form.

The basic ideas of the system are:

(*a*) the concept of class;

(*b*) the concept of the complement or negation of a class;

(*c*) the unique null class;

(*d*) the logical product of two classes;

(*e*) identity between classes.

The symbolism for (*a*) to (*d*) has been given above. (*e*) is symbolised by:

$$\text{(ix)} \qquad A = B.$$

To say that two classes A and B are identical is to say that every member of A is a member of B *and vice versa*. On this basis we may define the following equivalences:

(i) 1 eq. $0'$. Def. (In other words, the universe of discourse is the complement of the null class.)

(ii) $A + B$ eq. $(A'B')'$. Def.

(iii) $A \subset B$ eq. $AB' = 0$. Def.

The following laws hold for all classes in the system:

1. (*a*) $AA = A$.

   (*b*) $A + A = A$.

2. $A \subset A$.

3. If $A \subset B$ and $B \subset A$, then $A = B$.

4. If $A \subset B$ and $B \subset C$, then $A \subset C$.

5. (*a*) $AB = BA$.

   (*b*) $A + B = B + A$.

These are the commutative laws for addition and multiplication.

6. (*a*) $A (BC) = (AB) C$.

   (*b*) $A + (B + C) = (A + B) + C$.

These are the associative laws for logical multiplication and addition.

    7. (a) $A(B + C) = AB + AC$.

       (b) $A + BC = (A + B)(A + C)$.

These are the distributive laws.

    8. $0 \subset A \subset 1$.

    9. (a) $0A = 0$.

       (b) $1A = A$.

9 (a) states the obvious truth that there are no common members to any class and the null class. 9 (b) states the equally obvious truth that the members common to any class and the universe of discourse are the members of the first class.

    10. (a) $0 + A = A$.

       (b) $1 + A = 1$.

    11. (a) $AA' = 0$.

       (b) $A + A' = 1$.

This law states that (a) there are no members common to a class and its complement and (b) that the logical sum of any class and its complement exhaust the whole universe of discourse.

    12. (a) $(AB)' = A' + B'$.

       (b) $(A + B)' = A'B'$.

These are De Morgan's laws of duality.

    13. $(A')' = A$.

This is the law of involution or double negation.

These laws have been stated without proof and, indeed, in most cases, they will seem too obvious to need proof. But they can, of course, be set out systematically as an axiomatic system as was done in Chapter IV in the case of the propositional calculus.

It will probably have been noticed that some of these laws have an obvious similarity to certain laws of the calculus of propositions. (For example, 5, 6, 7, 12, and 13). The analogy is, in fact, a very close one as the calculus of propositions is just one interpretation of Boolean algebra. (The reader should try to trace for himself the correspondences between the terminology of the two systems.)

4. The Boolean Algebra of Classes and the Syllogism. The algebra of classes may be used to solve problems involving class relationships of considerable complexity though these applications are beyond the scope of this short treatment. (For further reading on this point, see the bibliography at the end of the section.) It may, however, be useful to see how it can be applied to solve the simple problems of class relationships presented by the classical syllogism.

In order to use the algebra of classes for the solution of logical problems, we have to apply the laws set out above in the manipulation and development of class expressions. An important type of manipulation is the development of a class expression in *canonical* or *normal form*. It will be remembered that in the calculus of propositions the expression of a truth-function in a conjunctive normal form constituted a decision procedure for the calculus. An analogous procedure for the class calculus is to express a class formula as a *sum* of *products* (that is, in a *disjunctive* normal form) such that each product which is a member of the sum contains all the class symbols involved in the expression, either negated or unnegated. Let us take for example a Boolean class expression F, say:

(1) $F = ((A'B) + C')'$.

We have to express this as a sum of products containing all the class symbols A, B, and C, either negated or unnegated, thus:

(2) $F = ABC + AB'C + A'B'C$.

The transformation from (1) to (2) is effected by the successive application of laws set out in Section 3 above, in particular (1), (7), (9), (11), and (12).

$$\begin{aligned}
F &= ((A'B) + C')' & \\
&= (A'B)'C & \text{by (12).} \\
&= (A + B')\,C & \text{by (12).} \\
&= (AC + B'C) & \text{by (7).} \\
&= 1\,(AC) + 1\,(B'C) & \text{by (9).} \\
&= (B + B')\,AC + (A + A')\,B'C & \text{by (11).} \\
&= ABC + AB'C + AB'C + A'B'C & \text{by (7).}
\end{aligned}$$

And, finally, dropping the duplicate $AB'C$ by (1) we have:

$$ABC + AB'C + A'B'C.$$

It will be seen that, in these expansions, products which are repeated, as $AB'C$ above, may be dropped by (1) and products which contain both a class symbol and its negation, as for example $AA'B'C$, are equivalent to 0 and may be dropped by (10).

The propositional forms of the classical logic may be translated into the notation of class algebra as follows:

All S is P :	$SP' = 0$.
No S is P :	$SP = 0$.
Some S is P :	$SP \neq 0$.
Some S is not P :	$SP' \neq 0$.

Thus, for example, " all men are mortal" becomes "the class consisting of the things which are both men and not-mortal is empty". And "some financiers are dishonest" becomes "the class of things which are both financiers and dishonest is not empty".

Let us now consider a syllogism, say, Cesare in Figure II.

P e M   No Christians are vice traffickers.

S a M   All dope peddlers are vice traffickers.

S e P   No dope peddlers are Christians.

This may be translated into the notation of the class calculus thus:

$$PM = 0$$
$$SM' = 0$$
$$SP = 0$$

Expanding the premisses and conclusion, we get:*

$$SMP + S'MP = 0$$
$$SM'P + SM'P' = 0$$
$$SMP + SM'P = 0$$

Combining the premisses we have:

$$SMP + S'MP + SM'P + SM'P' = 0.$$

And since the sum of these four classes is zero, the sum of any two of them is also zero, and in particular

$$SMP + SM'P = 0$$

which is the conclusion.

Let us now look at a syllogism with a particular premiss and, in consequence, a particular conclusion. The following is an instance of Dimaris in Figure IV:

P i M   Some ratepayers are voters.

M a S   All voters are citizens.

S i P   Some citizens are ratepayers.

---

* Notice that by (5) of Section 3, the commutative law, the order in which we write the terms in a logical product, is immaterial.

Translating this into the terminology of the algebra of classes, we have:

$$PM \neq 0$$
$$\frac{MS' = 0}{SP \neq 0}$$

Expanding the premisses and conclusion into normal form, we get:

$$SMP + S'MP \neq 0$$
$$\frac{S'MP + S'MP' = 0}{SMP + SM'P \neq 0}$$

Now we know from the minor premiss that $S'MP = 0$. Thus the major premiss is $SMP + 0 \neq 0$. Therefore, the class SMP must have members; that is $SP \neq 0$. And this is what the conclusion states. (Notice that from $SMP \neq 0$, we may deduce that $SP \neq 0$, but *not* conversely. For $SP \neq 0$ would be true if $SMP = 0$ and $SM'P \neq 0$.)

There are four of the syllogistic moods which are valid in the traditional logic but which cannot be proved to be valid by the algebra of classes. These are the syllogisms in which a particular conclusion is drawn from two universal premisses. The moods are Darapti and Felapton in Figure III and Bramantip and Fesapo in Figure IV. The reason for this is that in dealing with classes by the methods of Boolean algebra we do not make any assumptions as to whether or not the classes we are dealing with have members. But it was a tacit assumption of the traditional logic that all the classes mentioned in the argument had members. (See Chapter V, Section 12).

Each of the remaining fifteen valid moods may be validated in this way. It is, however, unnecessary to do this. For it can be shown that all these moods can be expressed without any loss of logical force in one of the two following forms. Each of these two forms can be proved by the method of expansion exemplified above.

(a)	(b)
$AB = 0$	$A'B = 0$
$B'C = 0$	$BC \neq 0$
$CA = 0$	$CA \neq 0$

(a) is the form applicable when the conclusion is universal and (b) when the conclusion is particular.

BIBLIOGRAPHICAL NOTE

APPENDIX

By far the best treatment of the classical syllogistic logic is given by Keynes (17). Other good expositions are in Joseph (15), Stebbing (28), Mace (22), and Bennett and Baylis (2). The last book also contains an excellent exposition of the algebra of classes. Elementary but very clear accounts of the algebra of classes will be found in Langer (19), Ambrose and Lazerowitz (1), Eaton (10), and Tarski (31). More detailed treatments are given by Lewis and Langford (20), Couturat (8), and Keynes (17), the last being somewhat hampered by an antiquated symbolism. The classical exposition is in Boole (5), developed by Jevons [(13) and (14)], and Venn (32). A very readable and entertaining approach is given in Lewis Carroll (6) but the symbolism used is clumsy and out-dated.

BIBLIOGRAPHY

(1) AMBROSE, A., and LAZEROWITZ, M., *Fundamentals of Symbolic Logic*, New York, 1948.

(2) BENNETT, A. A., and BAYLIS, C. A., *Formal Logic*, New York, 1946.

(3) BOCHENSKI, I. M., *Ancient Formal Logic*, Amsterdam, 1950.

(4) BOEHNER, P., *Medieval Logic*, Manchester, 1952.

(5) BOOLE, G., *Mathematical Analysis of Logic*, Cambridge, 1847, reprinted Oxford, 1948.

(6) CARROLL, L., *Symbolic Logic*, Fourth Edition, London, 1897.

(7) COOLEY, J. C., *Primer of Formal Logic*, New York, 1942.

(8) COUTURAT, L., *Algebra of Logic*, translated Robinson, London, 1914.

(9) DE MORGAN, A., *Formal Logic*, edited Taylor, London, 1926.

(10) EATON, R. M., *General Logic*, New York, 1931.

(11) FITCH, F. B., *Symbolic Logic*, New York, 1951.

(12) HILBERT, D., and ACKERMANN, W., *Principles of Mathematical Logic*, translated Hammond, Leckie, and Steinhardt, New York, 1950.

(13) JEVONS, W. S., *Principles of Science*, Second Edition, London, 1877.

(14) JEVONS, W. S., *Studies in Deductive Logic*, Second Edition, London, 1884.

(15) JOSEPH, H. W. B., *Introduction to Logic*, Second Edition, Oxford, 1916.

(16) JOHNSON, W. E., *Logic, Parts I and II*, Cambridge, 1921-2.

(17) KEYNES, J. N., *Formal Logic*, Fourth Edition, London, 1906.

(18) KLEENE, S. C., *Introduction to Metamathematics*, New York, 1952.

(19) LANGER, S. K., *Introduction to Symbolic Logic*, London, 1937.

(20) Lewis, C. I., and Langford, C. H., *Symbolic Logic*, New York, 1932.

(21) Lukasiewicz, J., *Aristotle's Syllogistic*, Oxford, 1951.

(22) Mace, C. A., *Principles of Logic*, London, 1933.

(23) Quine, W. V., *Mathematical Logic*, Revised Edition, Harvard, 1951.

(24) Quine, W. V., *Methods of Logic*, New York, 1950.

(25) Reichenbach, H., *Elements of Symbolic Logic*, New York, 1947.

(26) Rosenbloom, P., *Elements of Mathematical Logic*, New York, 1950.

(27) Russell, B. A. W., *Introduction to Mathematical Philosophy*, London, 1919.

(28) Stebbing, L. S., *Modern Introduction to Logic*, Sixth Edition, London, 1948.

(29) Stebbing, L. S., *Modern Elementary Logic*, Revised Edition, edited C. K. Mundle, London, 1952.

(30) Strawson, P. F., *Introduction to Logical Theory*, London, 1952.

(31) Tarski, A., *Introduction to Logic*, New York, 1941.

(32) Venn, J., *Symbolic Logic*, London, 1894.

(33) Whitehead, A. N., and Russell, B. A. W., *Principia Mathematica*, Vol. I, Cambridge, 1910, Second Edition, Vol. I, Cambridge, 1925.

(34) Copi, I. M., *Symbolic Logic*, New York, 1954.

(35) Leblanc, H., *Introduction to Deductive Logic*, New York, 1955.

EXERCISES

1. Clarify the logical form of the following arguments by substituting symbols for terms and propositions as shown in Section 2 of Chapter I. Which of the arguments have the same logical form?

(a) No naturalists are unobservant. Some unobservant people are interested in animals. *Therefore*, some people who are interested in animals are not naturalists.

(b) All shareholders are entitled to vote at the annual general meeting. All directors are shareholders. *Therefore*, all directors are entitled to vote at the annual general meeting.

(c) If England lose the test match, then the team will be changed. If the wicket is soft at Lord's, England will lose the test match. The team will not be changed. *Therefore*, there will not be a soft wicket at Lord's.

(d) No bats are feathered. All bats can fly. *Therefore*, some animals which can fly are not feathered.

(e) All ratepayers are entitled to vote in municipal elections. Some parliamentary electors are not entitled to vote in municipal elections. *Therefore*, some parliamentary electors are not ratepayers.

(f) If the truce negotiations succeed or the United Nations approve a disarmament plan, then armament shares will slump. Armament shares will not slump. *Therefore*, the United Nations will not approve a plan for disarmament.

(g) If atomic power can be widely applied in industry, then the coal mining industry will lose its importance. If the coal mining industry loses its importance, there will be an increase in unemployment. There will not be an increase in unemployment. *Therefore*, atomic power cannot be widely applied in industry.

(h) If it is false that prices will rise and taxes will not be reduced, then there will be increased spending. If there is increased spending, there will be a fall in national savings.

There will not be a fall in national savings. *Therefore*, it is false that either prices will not rise or taxes will be reduced.

(*i*) If there is a change of government, then confidence in the pound will not be restored. If confidence in the pound is not restored, then imports will be restricted. *Therefore*, if imports are not restricted, there will not be a change of government.

(*j*) If A's evidence is true, then B is not guilty. If B is not guilty, then C's evidence is perjured. *Therefore*, if C's evidence is not perjured, A's evidence is not true.

(*k*) All bishops are learned men. Some Christians are bishops. *Therefore*, some Christians are learned men.

(*l*) No defenders of democracy are fascists. All defenders of democracy are believers in human equality. *Therefore*, some believers in human equality are not fascists.

CHAPTERS II AND III

1. Construct truth-tables for the following propositional formulae. Which of them are tautologies?

(*a*) $p \supset (p \lor q)$.

(*b*) $(p \lor q) \supset p$.

(*c*) $p \supset (p.q)$.

(*d*) $(p.q) \supset p$.

(*e*) $(p.q) \supset (p \lor q)$.

(*f*) $((p \supset q) \supset r) \supset (p \supset (q \supset r))$.

(*g*) $(p \supset q) \supset (\sim p \supset \sim q)$.

(*h*) $(p \supset q) \supset (\sim q \supset \sim p)$.

(*i*) $((\sim p \supset \sim q) \supset \sim r) \supset \sim (p \supset (q \supset r))$.

(*j*) $((p \lor q) \supset r) \supset ((\sim p \lor r).(\sim q \lor r))$.

(*k*) $((p.q) \supset r) \supset ((\sim p.r) \lor (\sim q.r))$.

(*l*) $((p.q) \supset r) \equiv (p \supset (q \supset r))$.

(*m*) $((p \supset \sim q) \supset (\sim p \supset q)) \supset (p \supset r)$.

(*n*) $((p \supset q) \supset r) \supset ((r \supset p) \supset (s \supset p))$.

(*o*) $(p \lor q \lor r) \supset ((\sim p \supset r).(\sim q \supset r))$.

2. Reduce the formulae of (1) to conjunctive normal form.

3. Test the following arguments for validity by constructing the appropriate truth-tables:

(*a*) If Jones is guilty or the police are suspicious, then either Jones will bribe the police or he will not remain in town. *Therefore*, if Jones remains in town or the police are suspicious, it is false that he is both guilty and is not bribing the police.

(*b*) If Mr Moneybags takes penicillin and is properly looked after, he will recover. If he recovers, his relatives will be disappointed. His relatives will not be disappointed. *Therefore*, either he won't take penicillin or he won't be properly looked after.

(*c*) If there is an election, the government will not remain in power. Either the government will remain in power or there will be a *coup d'état*. There won't be a *coup d'état*. *Therefore*, there won't be an election.

(*d*) If A is elected, then B will resign. If C is elected, then B won't resign. If A is elected, then C won't be elected. *Therefore*, B will resign.

(*e*) If A is elected, then B will resign. If C is elected then B will not resign. *Therefore*, if A is elected, C won't be elected.

(*f*) If the price of gold shares falls or boring operations fail, then either Jones will go bankrupt or he will commit suicide. If the boring operations fail or Jones goes bankrupt, there will be a prosecution. There will not be a prosecution. The price of gold shares will fall. *Therefore*, Jones will commit suicide.

(*g*) If A resigns, the party will split and there will be an election. If there is an election, the international situation won't improve. The international situation will improve. *Therefore*, A won't resign.

(*h*) If the evidence was forged or the police are bribed, then A is not guilty. If the chief witness was not telling the truth, then the evidence was forged. If the chief witness was telling the truth, then A is guilty. *Therefore*, the police were not bribed.

(*i*) If it is false that A's flight implies A's guilt, then if the evidence was properly recorded, the police were not impartial. *Therefore*, if A has fled and the evidence was properly recorded, then, if the police were impartial, A is guilty.

(*j*) If the play is good and the acting is not incompetent, then either the public will respond or they cannot appreciate good theatre. *Therefore*, if the public can appreciate good theatre and the acting is not incompetent, if the play is good, the public will respond.

(*k*) If there is a slump or strikes increase, then Russia will grow stronger in Europe and America will not increase dollar aid. If there is a slump, Russia will not grow stronger in Europe. If there is not a slump, America will increase dollar aid. *Therefore*, strikes will not increase.

(*l*) He who hath wife and children giveth hostages to fortune. Jones is a bachelor. *Therefore*, Jones does not give hostages to fortune.

(*m*) If exports increase, then the labour situation will improve and there won't be a financial crisis. If there is no financial crisis, there will be no need to cut the armaments programme. It will be necessary to cut the armaments programme. *Therefore*, exports will not increase.

(*n*) If A beats B, then if he beats C he will also beat D and win the cup. He will beat C but he won't beat D. *Therefore*, A won't beat B.

(*o*) If the government is re-elected, then it is false that public confidence will be restored and trade will improve. It is false that either public confidence won't be restored or trade won't improve. *Therefore*, the government will be re-elected.

4. Test the validity of (*a*) to (*o*) of (3) above by the short truth-table method where this can be used.

5. Test the validity of (*a*) to (*o*) of (3) by reduction to conjunctive normal form.

6. Test the validity of the following arguments by the method of equivalent substitutions (see Chapter III, last section):

(*a*) If the cost of living rises or government revenues increase, then salary increases will be granted. No salary increases will be granted. *Therefore*, government revenues will not increase.

(*b*) If the police do not catch the murderer within a week, there will be a public outcry. If there is a public outcry, then the chief of police will resign. The chief of police will not resign. *Therefore*, the police will catch the murderer within a week.

(c) If the picture is not a forgery, then it is valuable. It is not the case that either it is a forgery or that it is not sought after by collectors. If the picture is not by Vermeer, then it is not sought after by collectors. *Therefore*, the picture is valuable and it is by Vermeer.

(d) If the insurance company refused the policy, then Messrs A have a bad reputation and the property is not valuable. If Messrs A have no insurable interest and the property is not valuable, then the proposed transaction is suspect. *Therefore*, if Messrs A have no insurable interest and the insurance company have refused the policy, then the proposed transaction is suspect.

(e) If A resigns, then either B will not be elected or C will demand an enquiry. If the newspapers get the story, then C will not demand an enquiry. If B is not elected, then C will demand an enquiry. The newspapers will get the story. *Therefore*, A will not resign.

(f) If, if there is not a good harvest, then the price of bread will rise, then if unemployment increases, there will be riots in the capital. *Therefore*, either there will be riots in the capital or unemployment will not increase, or the price of bread will not rise and it is true that either unemployment will not increase or there will be riots in the capital or there will be a good harvest.

(g) If the government falls, then, if the opposition are unprepared, either there will be a *coup d'état* or foreign powers will intervene. If there is a *coup d'état* or foreign powers intervene, then the opposition will not be unprepared. The opposition are unprepared. *Therefore*, the government will not fall.

(h) If the report is true or the journalists have not been bribed, then if the government denies the report, if the journalists have been bribed they will attack the government. *Therefore*, if it is false that if the journalists have been bribed and the government deny the report, the journalists will attack the government, then the report is not true and the journalists have been bribed.

(i) If, if the opposition win the election, there will be a boom on the Stock Exchange, then the government have lost the confidence of the electorate and they will not be re-elected. They will be re-elected. *Therefore*, the opposition will win the election.

(*j*) If either Jones was present or Brown was absent, then if the meeting was not postponed, the case will be unfairly presented. If either Brown was absent or the meeting was postponed, then there will be no public protest. Jones was present. There will be a public protest. *Therefore*, the case will be unfairly presented.

CHAPTER IV

1. Derive the following formulae from the rules and axioms given in Chapter IV:

(*a*) $p \supset (\sim q \supset p)$.

(*b*) $q \supset (p \supset q)$.

(*c*) $(p \supset \sim q) \supset (q \supset \sim p)$.

(*d*) $(q \lor p) \supset (p \lor q)$.

(*e*) $p \supset (q \lor p)$.

(*f*) $(p \supset q) \supset ((r \supset p) \supset (r \supset q))$.

(*g*) $p \supset (p \lor p)$.

(*h*) $(p \supset \sim p) \supset \sim p$.

(*i*) $(\sim p \lor \sim q) \supset \sim (p . q)$.

(*j*) $\sim (p . \sim p)$.

CHAPTER V AND APPENDIX

1. Using the decision procedure explained in Chapter V, Sections 11 and 12, test the validity of examples (*a*), (*b*), (*d*), (*k*), and (*l*) of Chapter I above.

2. Use this procedure to test the validity of the following:

(*a*) All members of the Church Assembly believe in the Thirty-nine Articles. All believers in the Thirty-nine Articles appreciate theological niceties. *Therefore*, all members of the Church Assembly appreciate theological niceties.

(*b*) No sharks are vegetarians. All large fish in Sydney Harbour are sharks. *Therefore*, no large fish in Sydney Harbour are vegetarians.

(*c*) All psychiatrists are credulous. Some scientists are not credulous. *Therefore*, some psychiatrists are not scientists.

(*d*) No neurotics have a well balanced personality. Some artists are neurotic. *Therefore*, some artists do not have a well balanced personality.

(*e*) All trade unions aim at the welfare of the working man. Some trade unions restrict industrial efficiency. *Therefore*, some organisations which restrict industrial efficiency aim at the welfare of the working man.

(*f*) No written examination is a safe test of merit. All written examinations demand considerable memory knowledge. *Therefore*, some tests demanding considerable memory knowledge are not safe tests of merit.

(*g*) All dishonest practices are socially undesirable. All gambling is socially undesirable. *Therefore*, some gambling is dishonest practice.

(*h*) All theories based on empirical evidence deserve rational consideration. Some psychological theories are not based on empirical evidence. *Therefore*, some psychological theories do not deserve rational consideration.

(*i*) All theories based on empirical evidence deserve rational consideration. Some psychological theories do not deserve rational consideration. *Therefore*, some psychological theories are not based on empirical evidence.

(*j*) No religious doctrines can be established by scientific evidence. Some religious doctrines command the assent of intelligent people. *Therefore*, some doctrines that command the assent of intelligent people cannot be established by scientific evidence.

(*k*) All babies are illogical. Nobody is despised who can manage a crocodile. All illogical persons are despised. *Therefore*, no babies can manage a crocodile. (Lewis Carroll.)

(*l*) No one takes in *The Times* unless he is well educated. No hedgehogs can read. Those who cannot read are not well educated. *Therefore*, no hedgehog takes in *The Times*. (Lewis Carroll.)

(*m*) No boys under twelve are admitted to this school as boarders. All the industrious boys have red hair. None of the day boys learn Greek. None but those under twelve are idle. *Therefore*, none but red-haired boys learn Greek in this school. (Lewis Carroll.)

(*n*) No kitten that loves fish is unteachable. No kitten without a tail will play with a gorilla. Kittens with whiskers always love fish. No teachable kitten has green eyes. No kittens have tails unless they have whiskers. *Therefore*, no kitten with green eyes will play with a gorilla. (Lewis Carroll.)

(*o*) No one who is going to a party ever fails to brush his hair. No one looks fascinating if he is untidy. Opium eaters have no self-command. Everyone who has brushed his hair looks fascinating. No one wears white kid gloves unless he is going to a party. A man is always untidy if he has no self-command. *Therefore*, opium eaters never wear white kid gloves. (Lewis Carroll.) (Hint: Let the universe of discourse be "persons": $A =$ going to a party, $B =$ having brushed one's hair, $C =$ having self-command, $D =$ looking fascinating, $E =$ opium eaters, $F =$ tidy, $G =$ wearing white kid gloves.)

3. Apply the rules of the classical syllogism given in the Appendix to test the validity of (*a*) to (*j*) of (2) above.

4. Use the methods of Boolean algebra to test the validity of the examples in (2) above.

5. Put the following Boolean expressions into normal form:

(*a*) $AB' + A'$.

(*b*) $A' + AC + ABC' + AB'C'$.

(*c*) $AB + A'C + C'$.

(*d*) $(AB + A'C')' + B$.

(*e*) $(A + D)' (B + C')' + AD$.

(*f*) $(AB + BC')' + B'C$.

(*g*) $(A + BC + A'D)' + A'C'$.

INDEX

PRINTED IN GREAT BRITAIN BY UNIVERSITY TUTORIAL PRESS LTD, FOXTON
NEAR CAMBRIDGE